Diseases That Plague Modern Man

DISEASES THAT PLAGUE MODERN MAN

A History of Ten Communicable Diseases

Richard Gallagher

1969   Oceana Publications, Inc./Dobbs Ferry, New York

Printed in the United States of America

CONTENTS

ACKNOWLEDGEMENT

Anyone now writing on the history of communicable disease must at some point speak to the people of the World Health Organization if he is to complete a satisfying and satisfactory job. My thanks to all those at WHO's Geneva headquarters and New York City liaison office (in the communicable diseases division, public information, water supply, immunology, vector control, health education, and supply services) for their time, effort, support, and friendship. They are too numerous to mention individually. I shall always owe each a great deal.

A Roman wall painting depicting a Greek physician (believed to be Galen) treating a soldier's wounded leg. Rome looted Greek medical technology for its own use and on this base developed concepts of disease control and built some of the Western world's first public health works such as the aqueducts and sewers.

Musée National, Naples.

I INTRODUCTION

"Dogs suffer from three diseases: lyssa, quinsy, and sore feet . . .Lyssa drives the animal mad, and any animal whatever, excepting man, will take the disease if bitten by a dog so afflicted. The disease is fatal to the dog itself and to any animal it may bite, man excepted. . ."

Lyssa is rabies, from the Greek, meaning "frenzy," and the statement is untrue. Man is not excepted from rabies. Indeed, he is most susceptible to its ravages. This whimsical and inaccurate description is significant for two reasons, however. One, the writer was Aristotle (384-322 B. C.). He set it down easily and without fear of challenge or error in his *Historia Animalium* around 335 B.C. It is the first known written attempt to identify one of the world's oldest communicable diseases. Two, it is a reminder that things have not changed.

The men of Aristotle's time were naive and ignorant concerning their communicable diseases. The men of the present are only less so. For example, we now know a great deal about rabies. We can now vaccinate and treat for rabies. Yet, it is still a fatal disease in many cases. Once the virus reaches man's brain, man always dies in a fit of pain and mental upheaval which is terrifying to behold. There are no recorded recoveries. Man still does not know enough to prevent this form of death. He still struggles with it.

This illustrates one of the main themes of this book. The history of communicable disease is the history also of one of man's longest uninterrupted wars. Man has flailed at his disease enemies since the first day the first man realized he was sick and had better do something because people around him felt sick also and were dying.

Because of the ignorance which has prevailed over the centuries, man does not always triumph. Sometimes he wins a battle, yes, such as the success in driving malaria completely from Sardinia for the first time in that island's history. But he has never come close to winning the war, that is, the dream of eradicating disease from the world completely.

1

Malaria again can prove an elastic enemy with great snap-back powers. In Vietnam, for example, a new strain infecting American troops resists the conventional antimalarial drugs and responds only to the "Old Grandma Remedy," quinine. Here man has been driven back to the positions he held hundreds of years ago when the cinchona tree bark, the source of quinine, was first found to be therapeutic.

The enemy even appears to grow stronger instead of weaker, its numbers increase. The communicable disease roster is longer now than it was even a quarter century ago.

This should not be viewed as discouraging, however. The increase represents progress in a perverse way. The new diseases are not necessarily new. They have existed a long time. Man simply did not know enough to identify them before. Now he does.

Onchocerciasis or "river blindness" is one such so-called new disease. This is a tropic disease transmitted by flies. It blinds the populations of entire villages. It would seem this is clearly a disease by itself. Yet, until only a decade or so ago, thinking was that it was not an entity, but a manifestation of other tropic diseases.

And for each addition there is at least one deletion. Many of the old diseases are now generally unfamiliar. Anthrax, a disease which fells men and animals, and which results in death from extreme shock, used to be frequent. Anthrax is now a medical oddity in many parts of the world. Such diseases have been contained ("controlled" is the term used in public health) so as to be ineffective as an enemy.

By definition a communicable disease is an illness caused by a specific agent or its toxic products. It arises through transmission of that agent or products from a reservoir to a susceptible host. Transmission is accomplished in one of two ways: (1) Directly from an infected person or animal. (2) Indirectly via an intermediate plant, animal, vector, or inanimate environment. (See glossary at end of book for definition of these terms.)

There are hundreds of them. The American Public Health Association lists 148 in its current *Control of Communicable Diseases in Man*, a book considered a basic primer of community management of diseases. One hundred forty-eight is but a part of the total number. Among these Gothic horrors are ten which are today a major threat to survival. Some of them number their current victims in the hundreds of millions. They are: cholera, influenza, leprosy, parasitic infections (bilharziasis and onchocerciasis, and malaria) plague, smallpox, tuberculosis, and venereal disease with emphasis on syphilis.

All ten, each separately, some together, at one time or another have kept nations from growing great. Malaria is one. It seldom kills outright, at most in ten per cent of cases. But it does sap a man. It has drained the strength and ambition of entire populations to such a degree they sometimes cannot even take in a harvest.

Sardinia is a classic case. Before World War Two this Massachusetts-sized Mediterranean island was rated by the U.S. Army as the third most malarious place in the world. From 1936 to 1938, 35 persons in every thousand were infected by the local mosquito carrier *Anopheles labranchiae*. The rate for the rest of Italy was only 2.5 per 1,000. It is felt that ten per cent of the population was reeling about at one time or another shivering or burning with malaria.

DDT spraying began in 1946, everywhere men in jeeps and on foot could reach. By December 1949 the mosquito carriers had apparently been eliminated from the island, for not one primary malaria case was reported that year. The World Health Organization has since declared the island 100 per cent free of malaria.

The Sardinia campaign cost $12,000,000, but the return has been far more than that. The saving in days' pay lost due to sickness well exceeds $12,000,000 annually.

Flies as well as mosquitoes fall under DDT. Infants no longer die regularly each summer in great numbers as they once did from fly-borne diseases. The annual summer wave of fly-borne intestinal infections is now only a painful memory. Ewes and cows produce more milk because they are no longer tortured by flies and ticks.

Farm output was boosted by drainage programs which restored swampy, insect infected lands to use. Even smugglers benefitted. They hove to in the small ports to have their vessels sprayed for they too lost days to malaria seizures.

The gamut of communicable diseased include some names how unfamiliar to most in the well-to-do, hygienic Western nations, for they are truly diseases of the impoverished and the backward. Trachoma is a virus infection causing eyes to burn, blur, and ooze constantly. The corneas develop deep scars.

The eyelids become lumpy and distorted. Trachoma strikes the young mostly and may bring blindness if untreated. Some suffer torture in countries the world over, including the United States. For many the only treatment is a knife with which to scrape the crusts from the eyelids.

One disease among the specific ten described here is smallpox, one of the easiest diseases to prevent and control today. Vaccination bestows leakproof immunity for three years. Vaccination is compulsory in most countries. In the United States every incoming traveler, whether citizen or foreigner, must show proof of vaccination within the previous three years.

Nonetheless, smallpox has wiped out large masses of humanity several times. It is still the most dangerous, most feared, and most carefully watched for of all communicable diseases. It kills four of every ten victims and is more contagious than even the common cold. For all that is known about it, science still suffers a knowledge gap as did Aristotle in his discussion of rabies. There is yet no treatment for smallpox. If a person contracts it, he runs the course of the disease and lives, or else he dies. Man's nonstop war with communicable disease is well documented. Malaria, for one, was known to the ancients only too well. Scholar agree no other influenced the flow of history and the destiny of nations more. Malaria killed Alexander the Great (356-323 B. C.) when Greece ruled the world, and Greek civilization was never as powerful again. Malaria was a prime contributor to the physical torpor that weakened Rome.

Trachoma is the "flaming eyes" condition which plagued pharaonic Egypt 4,000 years ago. It is mentioned in the Ebers papyrus written 15 centuries before Christ, the oldest collection of medical notes known.

The Chinese knew smallpox in 1,000 B. C., and they were possibly the first to experiment with smallpox immunization. They stuffed powdered pox scabs into their nostrils.

The plague which wasted medieval Europe is felt by some historians to have been partly responsible for the breakdown of the feudal system. The great pandemics buried so many that there was in some areas no system at all. Not enough rulers survived to manage it. During the post-medieval epidemic of 1625 in England a gallows was erected at Windsor to hang anyone who arrived from London, which was infected.

Some of the ten are but new discoveries or recent recognitions. In parts of the world where they prevail, however, they bear as much historical importance as the plague did to the European Middle Ages.

Onchocerciasis, for one, is held responsible for vast population shifts in northern Ghana. In the Volta River Basin alone according to a World Health Organization estimate in fall 1967, onchocerciasis had blinded some 100,000, mostly men. This represents ten per cent of the population.

In the last decade, young men of the area have been uprooting themselves from home to move to higher, hillier, onchocerciasis-free areas. The disease is less prevalent or even absent in the highlands. These men do not accept the inevitability of blindness as did their fathers. The young women are moving upland also. They do not wish to remain behind in a place where the only husbands they find will probably be blind.

The hurt to the land and the people is apparent. Fertile fields are depopulated of the very men needed to cultivate them. They are left to the blind who cannot. Whole villages are drained of life.

Near paranoia is the most depressing human reaction to some of these diseases. It is difficult to muster aid against a scourge felt to be too loathesome for words and impossible to cure.

Leprosy has been viewed since Biblical times as the "terror disease" which eats limbs off and which can be avoided only by exiling the afflicted and cured only by Divine Chance.

In World War Two there was persistent rumor among American forces of an island to which any man contracting leprosy would be exiled forever. No one speaking of the island ever seemed to know the longitude and latitude. No one ever personally knew a man who had been conventried there. There was no such place. Yet, the story of "Leper Island" was still being repeated long after the war ended.

All ten diseases, whether widely known or little known are vital world forces, then. What happens to nations and their growth depends heavily on what is done to cure, control and possibly eradicate these diseases in the future.

Three diseases are considered such threats that they are placed among those six known as "The Quarantinable Diseases" under International Sanitary Regulations. The 14th Century Venetians most likely coined the word "quarantine" by frequently imposing 40-day isolation periods on incoming ships during plague epidemics. The figure is felt to be of religious origin. Christ spent 40 days in the wilderness being tested and proven.

The "quarantinables" are: cholera, louse-borne relapsing fever, louse-borne typhus, plague, smallpox, and yellow fever. These are the ones almost all nations feel to be so serious that they deserve international observation. This book covers three: cholera, plague, and smallpox.

The English are on what amounts to constant standby alert concerning smallpox. In Britain there are several fully equipped hospitals standing isolated and empty against the day when there might be a smallpox outbreak. The English call this precaution their "shilling in the bank of good health."

All communicable diseases are caused by one of four things:

(1) Plantlike organisms (which means yeasts, molds, and bacteria). One is the tubercle bacillus, the rodshaped organism which causes tuberculosis.

(2) Animal organisms, generally protozoa, the one-celled creatures. Malaria is caused by one of several types of protozoan parasites. Some infections of animal nature are caused by worms.

(3) Viruses. Till recently living organisms and their toxins were thought solely responsible for infection. Today there is growing evidence that ultra-microscopic viruses are responsible and that some viruses are not living things. (Result: The term "infectious agent" is considered more correct than "organism" when speaking of certain diseases.)

(4) Rickettsiae. These are rodshaped, sometimes circular microorganisms found in ticks, lice, fleas, or mice. They live in body cells or free in the intestines. These creatures transmit infection from animals to man or other animals which then transmit them to man. Rocky Mountain spotted fever is one example of communicable disease of the rickettsia type. The category is named after an American pathologist, Howard Taylor Ricketts (1871-1810) who died studying typhus in Mexico.

All communicable diseases are transmitted in one of five ways:

1—DIRECT CONTACT, that is, the touching of a healthy person by an infected person, animal or other reservoir, the communicable disease being transmitted as a result. Personal contact includes kissing or sexual intercourse. Some diseases passed in this manner are known as "touching diseases." Syphilis is one and can be passed only by intercourse or intimate petting.

Direct contact diseases also number among them the fungus diseases which thrive on decaying vegetable matter, dung heaps, compost, etc.

2—INDIRECT CONTACT. This means exactly what it appears to mean, that is, transfer of infection from person to person via some contaminated object such as a toy, utensil, toilet article, clothing, bedding, surgical instrument, with a subsequent hand-to-mouth or hand-to-open-wound transfer of the communicable disease agent. Such inanimate objects are called fomites, from the Latin noun for tinder, used for starting fires.

3—BY VEHICLE. A vehicle can be water, food, milk, blood plasma, any substance serving as intermediate transport for an infectious agent from its reservoir to a susceptible victim, that is, host. The host becomes infected by eating or drinking, innoculation or by deposit of infectious material on his kin.

4—VECTORS. "Vector" comes from another Latin word, the verb *vehere*, to carry. Vectors then are simply carriers. They are usually arthropods, creatures having hard, jointed shells called exoskeletons and paired jointed legs. Mosquitoes and ticks are arthropods, vectors for many communicable diseases.

There are two kinds of vectors:

A-Biological vectors. A creature in whose body the infecting agent develops or multiplies before it can be infective to the human. Anopheles mosquitoes which transmit malaria, are biological vectors.

B-Mechanical vectors. Usually an arthropod carrying a disease parasite as though it is excess baggage, needed in the life cycle of the parasite.

5—AIRBORNE. This is another form of indirect contact. Infectious agents are transmitted from an infected to a "clean" person by air. They land on his skin or in open wounds. They float into the nose and mouth when the person breathes. The most common airborne transmission vehicle is the mucous droplet of the sneeze. Another is the particle of dust which arises from the floor, possibly contaminated by a sneeze. Bedding, clothes, soil, and dungheaps can give off disease agents. Smallpox is easily transmitted in this fashion, a fact which only adds danger to its deadly aspects.

All communicable diseases also have six reservoirs or sources of infection. They are (1) man, (2) animals, (3) insects, (4) plants, (5) soil, and (6) organic matter once more, such as manure heaps and compost.

It should be remembered that man generally is his own greatest reservoir and therefore his own greatest enemy. The more common and severe infections of man are caused by agents which breed and grow best in his own tissues. Man is the reservoir of disease agents which are more apt to be dangerous to him than to other species.

The communicable diseases drain the strength and/or kill the flesh and (almost always) destroy the morale and happiness of hundreds of millions.

The communicable diseases have one negative quality in their favor, however. They are not, as are old age and dying, inevitable. They are by-products of parasitical invasion and occupation. As such, they are subject to counterattack and rout.

Against some, man is born with, or later develops, a degree of natural immunity.

To combat others he can acquire or manufacture his own in two forms:

1—NATURAL IMMUNITY. The ability of a body to fight a specific infection under normal conditions is called natural immunity. "Normal conditions" are key words here. They mean the individual has never had the specific disease, nor has he ever been immunized against it. Yet he is immune to some degree. The history of tuberculosis illustrates one form of natural defense spoken of as "racial immunity."

The casualties tuberculosis claims among American Indians and Negroes in Africa is thought by some to be a manifestation of genetic weakness or susceptibility.

Tuberculosis, however, is new to Indians and Negroes, whereas it has been present among white people of Europe for centuries. These same colonizing whites brought it to the Indians and Negroes.

Over long exposure, death has eliminated whites susceptible to the disease. The hardier ones survived to breed generations of children less susceptible to the disease. The racial immunity passed along from one generation to another is a result of the natural selection described by Charles Darwin (1809-1882). It is not a manifestation of white superiority or Indian or Negro weakness. By long cohabitation with tuberculosis, whites have developed a higher resistance to it. Indians and Negroes have not lived with TB long enough to have done so as yet.

2—ACQUIRED IMMUNITY. Antigens and antibodies are the builders of acquired immunity. Both are necessary. To activate immunity the latter must cannibalize the former.

Antigens are substances (disease cultures sometimes) which stimulate the body (make it slightly ill) to produce the antibodies (disease fighters). Antibodies are the protective force (immunity) produced by a body stimulated with (infected by) antigens. The antibodies destroy the antigens.

Acquired immunity is of two kinds:

A—Active, or disease immunity developed when a human body contracts a disease and produces its own antibodies. The disease may enter naturally, as when a person has a mild diphtheria attack and develops immunity. Such defense is described as "naturally acquired."

Or, the antigen may be introduced artificially. Smallpox vaccination is the model artificial induction. A local infection is induced with a potent dose. The human body then manufactures its own antibodies. This is known as "artificial induction."

B—Passive Immunity. This is protection against diseases created by borrowed antibodies from some other person or animal. The recipient does not manufacture his own antibodies in response to an antigen invasion.

Immunity of this kind may be "naturally acquired" before birth, that is, antibodies cross from the mother to the fetus via the placenta.

It may also be "artificially induced." Any injection of antibodies from an already immune person or animal is artificial induction. Use of diphtheria antitoxin to afford two- to three-week protection is a case in point.

Active immunity, either natural or artificial, generally lasts and is considered permanent or semipermanent.

Passive immunity, again natural or acquired, is usually only temporary.

These breakdowns of infection, transmission, and immunity represent simplification of basic subject material to the extreme. There is far more to the study of communicable disease. Under "immunity" for example, *Dorland's Illustrated Medical Dictionary* lists 42 kinds.

This book will not explore such details. The biology student already knows them or will know which references supply them when needed. The student concerned only with the history of communicable disease will not require them.

*　　*　　*

What is the future of communicable disease?

Dr. V. Martinez Dominquez, a leprosy specialist with international organizations for three decades has observed, "Leprosy is a terrible disease but that's all it is, a disease. Not a myth or a horror. It can be dealt with." This holds true for all communicable diseases.

True, they are discouraging, frightening subjects; onchocereiasis with its threat of blindness for 20,000,000 can only be a horror. The communicable diseases are as international as fallout. They bully every person on earth.

On this premise, single governments, the treaty organizations, the large nonpolitical international health bodies are moving ahead. The bulk of the work will probably fall more and more to the latter, the famous ones such as the Pan American Health Organization and the World Health Organization, the lesser-known with curious names such as the British Empire Society for the Blind. The global approach has become essential. Only in global effort can global diseases be dealt with. This has become increasingly plain over the past 100 years, since the first international conference was called on cholera in Paris in 1851. Twelve states sent representatives to that conference to discuss the problem which required "the combined consideration and effort of more than one country."

Old approaches are being reexamined. Epidemic control by classic measures such as quarantine is giving way to the principle of epidemic prevention. Disease is sought where it festers before it breaks out, a principle known as surveillance. Analogy to fire is often made concerning communicable disease, namely, it is easier and less costly to prevent fires than it is to fight them after they break out.

In the future the international health groups will look further into:

● Prediction and selection of insecticides to kill strains of pests which have not yet appeared.

● Genetic manipulation of insect vectors, either to render them noncarriers or else breed them out of existence by damaging their chromosomes.

● Immunization agents for diseases such as leprosy.

● Chemotherapy, the treatment of disease with both serums and drugs, a relatively new attack angle on the communicables.

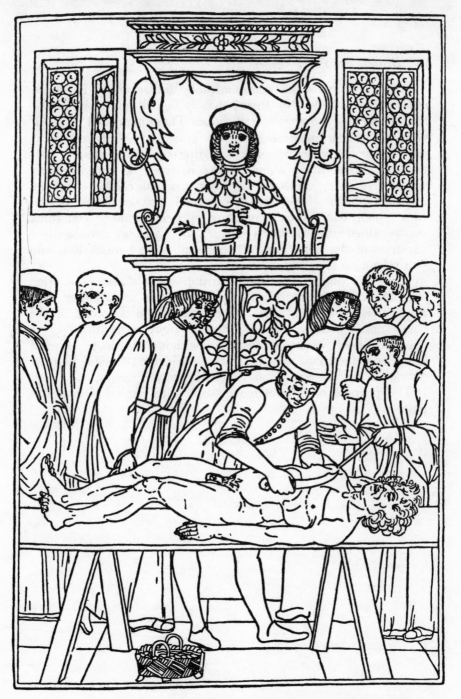

A medieval anatomy lesson. It was common for the professor to read instructions aloud from a pulpit-like dais while someone else (often a local barber) performed the dissection. Frequently, neither paid attention to the other. Such inefficient practice prevailed on all levels of medicine. Result: Knowledge of anatomy, pharmacy, communicable disease was filled with error and fancy. World Health Organization

● Eradication of all communicable disease using the above means and others. No theory has polarized views in public health recently more than eradication. Those impressed by DDT victories against malaria feel it is possible. Others feel 'total eradication' is something like squaring the circle, that is, impossible. "One thing about nature is, she'll do her damndest to preserve everything she's already put on this earth," observed a WHO official. "And this bloody well includes disease organisms which don't even have any apparent value. You think you've killed the mosquito vector, say, and up pops a slight variation of the same one and your stuff doesn't touch him and you've got to start again."

There are other problems. Nutrition is one. Large population shift to cities where disease probability soars are another. Still another is persuading the "have" nations to do more for the "have-nots" because they also have a right to health.

Men cannot work on the future without knowledge of what has gone before. Past mistakes such as Aristotle's fanciful blunder on rabies are the things on which the future moves.

The purpose of this reference work is to retrace part of this past.

". . . a man does not last out eight hours' time. . . ."

The epidemic diseases present one of the confounding mysteries of medicine:

Why do they periodically appear, rage and take large tolls, then fade away, sometimes to reappear in a few years, sometimes to vanish forever?

On the one hand we know so much. The causes of epidemic diseases themselves are no longer mysterious. The pathways they take in spreading are clearly marked: respiration, ingestion, animal bites, and personal contact. The means of controlling disease are familiar, in some instances, practiced for centuries: immunization, sanitation, isolation, and treatment.

On the other we know so little. There are still no explanations of the advent and farewell of epidemic diseases. Still undetermined is the relationship between disease pathogenicity and human vulnerability, a complex formula which seems to determine when man will (or will not) be tortured and destroyed.

"Souvenirs of Cholera."
An etching
by Honore Daumier
(1809-1879).

ǀ Cholera is one of the most perplexing of all. The disease travels under several names: Asiatic cholera, Indian cholera, algid cholera and asphytic cholera, to name some. In 1906 a new strain was identified, named, and added to the list, that of El Tor. El Tor is the name of the quarantine station on the Red Sea where this particular vibrio was first isolated in 1905 in pilgrims returning from the Mecca pilgrimage.

Cholera, as the parts of its name indicate, brings on violent vomiting (from the Greek *chole* , standing for bile and biliousness), and loose "rice water" diarrhea (*rein,* to flow).

An infectious disease caused by spirilla (bacteria) shaped like a letter "S" or a comma, in adults, cholera also brings on painful muscle cramps in arms and legs, falling bodily temperature, clammy sweat, fierce thirst, feeble pulse and blood pressure, arrested circulation, sunken cheeks and eyes, and often coma and death. In infants, temperatures run high, 105-108°F. The end result also is often death.

Its home since earliest recollection has been Asia (hence the common name, Asiatic cholera) where it has several homes, actually. Cholera has long been endemic in and around the Ganges Delta of India. Now the Celebes Sea Islands have been identified as a focus of the El Tor strain.

Without warning cholera has swept out from this traditional home often in pandemics which have buried uncountable millions in Asia, Africa, the Middle East, and on occasion parts of Europe and the Western Hemisphere.

Just as swiftly, without warning, it has retreated, leaving behind little to explain why it came, and little to say when it will come forth again. It has established few visible patterns. It has permitted little predictability except to say that in the tropics it is more prevalent during rainy seasons. No single factor can be held responsible for the intermittent onslaughts. ⱪ

Its ability to confound is also what makes it one of medicine's most difficult, terrifying communicable disease foes. Just when cholera was believed to be on the verge of extinction, a new pandemic broke out in 1961 and invaded 20 countries, as far west as Iran and Iraq.

ⱪCholera is one of the six quarantinable diseases covered by the International Sanitary Regulations administered by WHO. These regulations were adopted in 1951 by the World Health Assembly. They govern all international travel today. Under them most nations agree to screen all persons from areas where cholera is known to lurk, and to subject airplanes, ships, trains, and motor vehicles to broad search and decontamination. The intent of the International Sanitary Regualtions is clear and simple: to limit the spread of the six scourges by international cooperation.†

International cooperation.

If any one of the six is responsible for the current alliance against disease, it is cholera and the long memory of its capricious pandemics. Fear of continuing cholera pandemics was the principal reason for calling the early international sanitary conferences in the 19th century. Cholera was the subject discussed and argued most. And when the conferences ended, cholera was the disease about which all agreed most had to be done.

This is no wonder. Throughout history the "S" shaped cholera spirillum has been a deadly and mysterious enemy.

﹡﹡﹡

Backtracking to find ancestral material on communicable diseases can be a barren journey. Descriptions are inaccurate, fanciful, superstition-laden, and vague.

One of the nine plagues promised the Egyptians by Moses is described in the Book of Exodus, chapter eight, verse 17: "Aaron stretched out his hand with his rod and smote the dust of the earth and it became lice in man, and in beast. . . ." This may or may not indicate an epidemic of louse-borne typhus.

Sphyphilis was once thought to result from sexual intercourse between men and mares suffering from glanders.

Chronicling of disease has been ignored. Tales of the wars of antiquity make little mention of epidemics, yet they must have occurred. The armies were large; the generals knew little of sanitation. One explanation for absence of something so certain is found in the outlooks and beliefs of men of this time. A plague would have been seen as a visitation of the gods, something to be expected in life, rather than as an epidemic worthy of study and note.

Some diseases were quite honestly overlooked for centuries for a variety of reasons; no reliable people to record them for one, a gap in diagnostic technology for another. They often appear now as "new diseases." Yellow fever is one. It may well have raged for centuries in the West Indies and Latin America, but the first sound written description of this moquito borne affliction did not appear until Jean-Baptiste Dutertre (1610-1687) chronicled the outbreaks on Guadeloupe and St. Kitts in 1635.

Cholera suffers from this communicable disease of vagueness as much as any other, going back to the Golden Age of Greek medicine in the fifth and fourth centuries B. C.

The *Epidemics* attributed to the Greek Hippocrates (460?-377 B. C.) record neat, fact-laden eyewitness histories of actual cases. The seven *Epidemics* fall in the *Corpus Hippocraticum* (Latin, literally meaning the body of Hippocratic medical literature). Though much of this is now classified as medical curiosa, the *Corpus Hippocraticum* is, by virtue of the name it bears, a venerable collection of documents. It is also an historical whodunnit.

The collection bears imprints of many authors. It is impossible to say even who was the bearded, endlessly inquisitive "Father of Medicine," for he represents a puzzle himself. Verified details of his life and teaching are disappointingly few.

The number of volumes *Corpus Hippocraticum* contains is also in question; depending upon biographers, the count is 38, 53, 72, 130. Some are considered genuine works of Hippocrates, but only some.

The seven *Epidemics* contain case histories describing classical disease symptoms. They were almost certainly written by several different persons but are remarkably alike in spirit and attention to detail. Typical is the description of the agony of one Herophrontos.

Herophrontos was ablaze with an acute fever. His stool was watery and bile colored, the classic "rice water" symptom of Asiatic cholera. He felt gut-wrenching urgency to move his bowels though his body was drained of wastes. Even a slight touch caused great pain in his abdominal muscles. On the fifth day of his fever Herophrontos began to ooze sweat. Eventually he collapsed.

The *Epidemic* books gives Herophrontos' affliction no label clinically recognizable today. It is possible it was cholera, though many historians judge it to have been dysentery or typhoid fever because no epidemic is recorded during that time. The disease is so contagious that where one case occurs, general outbreak often follows if sanitation is bad.

Ancient clinical descriptions are often so ambivalent that they could be applied to any one of several diseases. Lack of epidemic notation should not necessarily fault the Hippocratic cholera description, however.

C. N. MacNamara (1832-1918) wrote in his milestone *History of Asiatic Cholera* that ancient chroniclers". . .have left us equally vivid accounts of this form of cholera in the various countries in which they lived. . . . But the more carefully we study the writings of these early authorities, the clearer it becomes that they had never met with cholera in its epidemic form."

*　　*　　*

The oldest known form is classic Asiatic (or epidemic) cholera caused by *Vibrio cholerae*. It probably appeared first in India. This nation is still an endemic focus and still sorely afflicted.

When in trouble man turned to his gods as well as his physicians. The ancients of what is now Lower Bengal worshipped a goddess of a disease, probably cholera. The fact that religion was sought to deal with a disease is circumstantial evidence of its epidemic proportions.

According to legend this goddess of cholera first appeared as a large stone in a forest to a wandering woman. Subsequent worship of the goddess through this stone was considered the only means of warding off epidemics.

It was stated earlier that ancient historians recorded little of epidemics decimating armies. Men in the field sometimes did, however. A Greek notation of a frightful epidemic was inscribed on a monolith by some soldier or officer in the invading force of Alexander the Great (356-323 B. C.) penetrating India. The inscription, patently referring to classic cholera, states:

> The lips blue, the face haggard, the eyes hollow, the stomach sunk in, the limbs contracted and crumpled as if by fire, those are the signs of the great illness which, invoked by a malediction of the priests, comes down to slay the braves. . .

The first irrefutable proof of cholera's existence acceptable to the scientific community was written by a European, an outsider visiting India, who possibly had never even heard of the disease before he observed it laying to waste the Malabar Coast of

India on the Arabian Sea. This appeared in *Lendas da India* (Legends of India) by historian Gaspar Correa (15?-1560). Correa was one of those inquisitive Europeans who could not stay away from this new unplumbed land discovered by the Portuguese navigator Vasco da Gama (1469?-1524) in 1498. Correa noted several striking epidemic aspects of a disease there. Unlike the vague references of antiquity, Correa's work named places and dates which could be corroborated by other sources.

One aspect particularly impressed Correa. In spring of 1503 there was a high death rate in the army of the sovereign of Calcutta. The fatalities were caused by a number of things, Correa noted, "by the current spring diseases, and smallpox besides which there was another disease, suddenlike, which struck with pain in the belly, so that a man did not last out eight hours' time." The "suddenlike" disease was indisputably cholera. The mention of this with the "current spring diseases, and smallpox" is significant. Epidemics are often visitations of several diseases simultaneously.

Few reporters were as disciplined and accurate as Correa, however. For the next three centuries, some 64 outbreaks were recorded. Some were accurate. Most were shot through with fancy and inaccuracy.

English physicians in India, for example, saw cholera as merely a spasmodic annoyance.

The Chinese, wasted by cholera from probably the seventh century onward, referred to a condition named "huo luan." This is today the Chinese term for cholera but centuries ago it covered a mixed bag: gastro-intestinal infections, colic, appendicitis, to name some besides cholera.

Arabic medical writers had no word for cholera at all.

It is almost certain cholera did not spread west from India before the 19th century. Fever exhibiting classic cholera symptoms appeared in London from 1679 to 1682. Indeed, it was even called cholera. Yet, it lacked the one characteristic, and this has led historians to believe it was not cholera. The spread did not reach epidemic proportions.

The history of cholera to the beginning of the 19th century, fragmentary and unreliable as it sometimes is, is clear on two points:

1—Cholera survived antiquity in its original form in India and reminded Indians of its presence periodically with raging displays of pestilence. No casualty figures are available, of course, but conservative estimates put fatalities at several hundred thousand yearly.

2—Religious pilgrimages and military operations (finally, after centuries) were credited with playing villainous roles in the spread of the disease. Quite simply, where there is endemic cholera, poor sanitation, and shifting masses of people (such as the thousands who flocked to Indian religious fairs, or the British colonial battalions), the odds favor an epidemic to follow. These are the elements on which cholera spawns and grows.

Until the 19th century cholera was considered by most of the world as a localized Indian concern only, something as inevitable in the way of life there as flies and sacred cows. It was a nuisance held to be of little concern to anyone else at all.

1817 changed all that. That year marked the beginning of the first of six cholera pandemics which spread death almost everywhere on earth. The attack was so rapid and virulent that many Europeans in particular did not even recognize cholera as cholera. They believed the disease then breeding in Bengal to be a brand new one.

*   *   *

The first pandemic began with a mistake over a supply of rice.

In 1817, India was drenched by rains. On August 23, the civil surgeon of a town named Jessore 50 miles northeast of Calcutta reported to his superiors that a "new" disease called "morbus oryzeus" or rice disease (from the Latin *morbus*, disease, and the Greek *oryzame*, rice) was then being observed in his district. It seemed to affect the gastrointestinal tract in a harsh way. Victims collapsed in seizures of vomiting and diarrhea. He guessed the victims contracted morbus oryzeus by eating rice which had been spoiled by damp and rain.

There were warnings that this was more than food poisoning. On September 17 a Calcutta magistrate reported the mere bellyache morbus oryzeus had "of late been far more fatal than at any former period within the recollection of the oldest inhabitants, running its course generally within a few hours and sometimes in a few minutes." Victims were dying on the same day they fell ill.

Within three months medical men and public health officials knew something was happening which they had never seen before. In Bengal province alone almost 200,000 square miles were blanketed with cholera cases. Hardly a town or village was without dead to mourn. Europeans in this area had never seen such devastation and suffering, which accounts for many of them mistaking the cholera for a new disease.

The cholera attacked everyone, all castes, all nationalities, all ages. Once more the susceptibility of large armies was demonstrated. A British Army group under the Marquis of Hastings (1754-1826), governor-general of India, lost more men simply marching through Bengal than it probably would have lost in a major engagement. Troops collapsed from their columns and writhed at the roadsides, vomiting and soiling themselves. Men who stooped to help often fell beside them. Wagons followed the troop column. The well loaded the sick aboard. When the sick died they were dumped out again to make room for still other sick men. In a diary entry made November 17, 1817, the marquis estimated, "Above 500 have died since sunset yesterday."

Casualties were enormous, in the tens of thousands in many areas. Thus it spread. The infection reached out to Ceylon, Java, Borneo, and other Indonesian islands in 1819 or 1830; actual dates are uncertain. Java was hit particularly hard; 100,000 died.

Sailors were the culprits. They brought it to Japan from Java and in Nagasaki and Osaka, the toll was so terrible masses were said to weep in grief. Exact figures are scarce; reliable reporting was lacking in this country also.

In 1921 cholera appeared in Basra, then the main port at the head of the Persian Gulf. Three weeks later, 18,000 were dead. From there the infection moved to Baghdad, carried by boat on the Tigris River, and by camel back in caravans. In a way, its arrival was timely from Baghdad's point of view. It felled and killed thousands in a Persian army then besieging the city.

North, west, and east the cholera moved. In so doing it made two spectacular overwater leaps to lands never before infected. One was the island Mauritius. In 1819, an epidemic killed 6,000, mostly Negro slaves. The second leap brought it to Africa in 1820 or 1821. The first cholera pandemic raged for six years from 1817 to 1823 according to one estimate. (Dates vary from source to source.) During the next six years it put hundreds of thousands in their graves.

Signs of letting up in Persia, Ceylon, Burma, and China were misread by many health authorities. They felt the disease was retreating to its traditional home in Lower Bengal (which it was) to stay forever (which it wasn't). Europe itself was felt out of danger of infection. This was also poor judgment.

The infection had reached Astrakham on the Volga Delta in Russia, but its grip was brief and its touch light. The harsh cold of winter 1823-1824 checked the vibrio. Cholera does not thrive in freezing weather.

The disease had only been driven into dormancy, however. It had not been wiped out as believed. It needed only proper conditions to flare to life once again in Europe's underbelly.

* * *

The second pandemic came out of India on caravans in 1828 and 1829. While information from this period is still scanty it is certain that cholera was raging in along the Ganges in 1827 and that in 1829 it was infecting Afghanistan and Persia. From there the caravans evidently carried cholera futher to European Russia. It flowed into Europe through Orenburg on the Ural River and from there to the Americas on the immigrant flow in a matter of a few months.

Governments learned that strict quarantine measures and *cordons sanitaires* proved effective when ruthlessly enforced on small scale. Some 10,000 of the Russian royal court isolated themselves at the imperial residences of Peterhof and Tsarskoye Selo in 1830-31, for example. Not one courtier contracted cholera.

Large scale quarantine was not so successful. Example:

Russia's western neighbors also established quarantine lines and the Austrian border in the early 1820's was described thus by one writer:

> This line contained at intervals of about 3,000 paces highly situated guard houses; the intervals between these were filled by patrols. The guards had loaded rifles; the officers were mounted. The guards had to watch day and night that neither human beings and cattle nor goods broke through the cordons. Everything that wanted to pass the frontier had to do so at certain stations. . .

Violators were promised harsh punishment and shooting, but risked death and sneaked through. The quarantines were increased from the traditional 40 days to 60 and even 100 days. Goods and belongings felt to carry cholera were burned. Still, these cordons failed, perhaps because their size made them unwieldy, and the disease spread.

"Vomiting Death" reached Moscow in 1830. From there it flooded the Baltic states and moved further west into Europe. Prussia, a country which enforced tight quarantine, could not plug all the leaks and took heavy casualties. In London in June 1831 the disease manifested itself aboard line ships of the Royal Navy anchored below London near merchant ships from Riga, the Baltic port now the capital of Latvia. The Riga ships were in quarantine at the time, suspected of carrying cholera.

Some of the fleet units later put in at Sunderland on England's west coast. Later, several cholera cases appeared in this city. By year's end in 1832, some 14,790 Englishmen had been struck down in an epidemic fanning out from Sunderland. Of these 5,432 died.

An outburst in Mecca in 1831 took 12,000 pilgriums to their deaths.

Belgium lost almost 8,000 people in 1832.

Cholera crossed the Atlantic:

● Canada in 1832, brought in on ships at quarantine at Grosse Island near Quebec. Total deaths in that city in two weeks: 1,000.

● To the United States in 1832, from Canada, via Chicago (then Fort Dearborn) and down the Mississippi valley. (The vibrio went west later with the wagons to California.)

● To Peru and Chile in 1832, Mexico, 1835.

● To Cuba, 1835, and from Cuba, back to the United States, besetting New Orleans and Charleston, S.C.

One date given for the end of the second pandemic is 1837. Pandemics, like floods, do not just dry up in a day. They subside gradually. Thus it was with cholera.

The 1837 phaseout date is subject to debate, therefore. Cholera continued to scourge the earth for several more years. It showed cyclic patterns, disappearing as suddenly as it came, then reappearing a few years later. England, the Middle East and eastern Europe were beset again and again during this second pandemic.

In 1849 New York City was figuratively a funnel through which cholera poured into the United States. Mortality topped 15 percent in some afflicted areas. The known Asiatic origin of the disease is held responsible in part for the strong sentiment against the Chinese which later prevailed in the country.

Misconception and ignorance were cholera's traveling mates. For instance, even sophisticated, knowledgeable Americans believed cholera a disease of gluttons, boozers and perverts. Sexual excess was said to weaken and "artificially stimulate" a person, leaving him defenseless against cholera. Prostitutes were thought to be particularly susceptible.

Story after story was told to bolster these contentions. In one house in New York 13 prostitutes contracted cholera and ten died. For so-called respectable people death from cholera was death with a hint of dishonor.

Two significant things came in Europe during this second pandemic. One was the discovery of the causal organism. Felix Pouchet (1800-1872) reported finding *vibrios* in the stool of cholera patients in France in 1849. At the time, however, Pouchet's discovery conveyed little of value to public health; it was just one more little understood fact about a yet-to-be understood disease.

The second was the fascination of one John Snow with a particular public water pump at Broad and Cambridge Streets in London in 1848-1849. Snow was born in 1813 and died in 1858. His career, though short, was productive. He proved the value of anesthesia in childbirth and surgery when this practice was considered a black art. He later became the world's first professional anesthetist, serving as such for Queen Victoria. Epidemics troubled him and in attempting to learn something about the cholera ravaging England his attention was drawn to the Broad Street pump.

There was good reason. Within a 250-yard radius, 500 suddenly died of cholera within ten days. It was probably the worst local outbreak ever in the country; no medieval plague was known to have taken so many lives in so small an area. Yet, the neighborhoods served by other public pumps were dealt with leniently by cholera. One listed only ten victims and five of these had drunk water from the Broad Street pump at one time. Many of the Broad Street pump victims were workers who mixed water with their drinks at nearby taverns. Others were people who liked the water and effervescing powder mixtures sold in sweet shops as sherbets. One particularly tragic case was that of a man who went to the home of a brother who had just died of cholera. While there he drank some brandy and water from the Broad Street pump. He too died the next night.

To John Snow these deaths linked to the Broad Street pump meant but one thing. In a milestone book *On the Mode of Communication of Cholera* he described how cholera is transmitted via water supplies and sewage systems. Snow was the first to understand cholera as a waterborne disease. His description is as valid today as when published in 1849, as the following small portion of it indicates:

> . . . when the water of a river becomes infected with the cholera evacuations emptied from on board ship, or passing down drains and sewers, the communication of the disease . . . is much more widely extended . . . I know of no instance in which it has been generally spread through a town or neighborhood, among all classes of the community, in which the drinking water has not been the medium of its diffusion. Each epidemic of cholera in London has borne a strict relation to the nature of the water supply of its different districts, being modified only by poverty and the crowding and want of cleanliness which always attend it.

Snow personally saw to it that the handle of the Broad Street pump was removed. The epidemic stopped that day.

Cholera showed signs of burning out again in 1851. In North Africa only Morocco was suffering. In Europe outbreaks occurred only in Poland, Silesia and Pomerania. The hopeful signs were repeated elsewhere.

Once again they were false signs.

Once again cholera was only waiting.

*   *   *

The subsequent four pandemics were much like the first two.

They varied only in spread (new countries stricken, old ones spared), numbers of victims (far greater), and transmission speed (much swifter). This last is important. As sea and land transportation technology broadened and grew, it created faster vehicles for cholera and other diseases to ride.

The third pandemic commenced in 1852. Once again India was the villain. The third ended, to give it an historical date, in 1859. But for localized brushfire eqidemics, worldwide spread of cholera appeared to have broken. At the end of the year, Europe seemed free of cholera.

The fourth pandemic came to life in 1863. It took brutal tolls. The figures were larger than ever before; not only did more die, fewer deaths were overlooked. The reporting machinery had vastly improved.

- More than 90,000 Moslem pilgrims died in Mecca in 1865.
- In 1866, there were 90,000 deaths in Russia.
- Sardinia lost 130,000 in 1867.
- In Zanzibar 70,000 died in 1869.
- Guadeloupe, 1865-66, 12,000 dead in a population of 150,000.
- In the United States the year 1866 ended with 50,000 dead. New York City listed 2,000 fatalities for summer and autumn 1866, a figure certainly well below the true one. Nowhere else outside the United States was the link between cholera spread and improved transportation made more obvious. The country was building a net of railroads west and cholera quickly followed the trunk lines.

Nor was the link between the disease and large armies ever made clearer. During the Civil War marshalling centers became distribution points as men came in "clean" and left infected, to carry the vibrio wherever their orders took them.

So deadly was the disease considered in China that there was a saying among people who lived on the rivers: "Should a man fall in, do not bother to help him out. He will die anyway." The rivers were often polluted with *Vibrio cholerae*.

In 1875 Hungary buried some 190,000 cholera dead. In 1877-79 China (accuracy of the records to be doubted) reported 158,204 cases, 89,207 of these dead.

These represent some of the peak figures. The disease receded once again at about this time and in 1879 the pandemic was considered finished.

The fifth pandemic lasted from 1881 to 1896 and two things grace its otherwise gloomy history. First it was gentler than previous pandemics; victims were fewer. Second, the German bacteriologist, Robert Koch, made a breakthrough unmatched before or since in cholera epidemiology. He isolated and identi-

Chasing cholera from Marseilles. In early 19th century
France, street crowds often danced about huge bonfires set to
"burn cholera from the air."

Harper's Weekly, November 18, 1865

fied the organism which causes the disease. The story has been told often and detailed accounts appear elsewhere. Briefly, Koch (1843-1910) was studying outbreaks in Egypt and India in 1883. From the stool of cholera victims in both places, he cultured "S" and comma-shaped bacilli now known as *Vibrio cholerae.*

That these organisms were somehow linked to cause of the disease was indicated as follows:

1. Their appearance by the millions in the feces of infected persons.

2. Fatal infection of guinea pigs with *Vibrio cholerae.*

That these organisms actually caused the disease in man was proven beyond doubt by clinical tests, that is, vaccination of human volunteers with pure *Vibrio cholerae* cultures.

Koch buried forever the argument between "contagionists" (those who insisted correctly cholera is a communicable organism-caused disease) and "localists" (who maintained cholera and other diseases were brought about by unwholesome environmental conditions and "bad air"). What Pouchet had started 40 years earlier, Koch completed.

Immunization programs began shortly after Koch's discovery in Spain and India with oral as well as needle vaccines.

The discovery was of little solace to Russia, however. There in the Volniya-Podolsk area in 1893-94 it claimed 800,000.

The discovery was of great irritation to certain mercantile and maritime nations. Traditionally they fought the contagionists. They claimed quarantine and other international restrictions on shipping and trade during cholera outbreak to be useless. They wanted nothing to interrupt the flow of goods and money. Koch's discovery was a setback. Proof of contagion meant that quarantine was valid as a weapon against contagion.

The sixth pandemic which began in 1899 is said by some authorities to have lasted until 1923. It almost positively came once more from India.

Again, cholera particularly brutalized the Mecca pilgrims. Indeed, death figures at this holy city rose with each decade. Four thousand died there in February, 1902, for example. Improved transport was again something which could be blamed for the jump.

In earlier times when polgrims moved by slow caravan, those carrying the disease either died from it or got over it before reaching the city. Time required for sailing voyages was shorter than the running time of the disease in many cases steamships were faster still. Worshippers who boarded the boat with cholera often got off the boat with it.

Individual ignorance could still be blamed, however. One outbreak in 1902 was traced to an old believer who brought a can of water from a Mecca well reputed to be holy to his home village. He wished to bring something of the pilgrimage to neighbors who could not make the pilgrimage themselves. He poured this water into the village well so all could benefit and touched off an epidemic which killed 42,000 Egyptians.

The Russian composer Peter Ilich Tchaikovsky (1840-1893) died of cholera in this sixth pandemic.

India took enormous casualties: 682,649 in 1906, 579,814 in 1908, 556,533 in 1918, 565,166 in 1919.

World War One fell within the timespan of pandemic six. The affinity between cholera and large troop bodies was again indicated by the fact that where sanitation and immunization measures were sound, the cholera level remained low. The German army with its strict anticholera programs suffered few cholera casualties. Where the measures were lax cholera figures jumped. Austria, which took in numbers of Russian and Serbian war prisoners without careful supervision, was hit hard.

Fumigation of travelers. In the late 19th century, French public health people believed they could arrest cholera by exposing travelers to unpleasant chemical fumes in special "plague rooms" in railroad, shipping terminals.

Scientific American Supplement, September 6, 1884.

It should be noted that different historians place different dates on beginnings and endings of the pandemics. For example, some authorities reject 1923 as the cutoff date of the sixth pandemic and say it ended as early as 1910. Some also maintain there were five pandemics in the 19th and early 20th centuries, not six.

Whatever the actual dates and numbers, mankind went through almost unbroken siege in a 100 years' war with cholera.

*   *   *

Though victims of the sixth pandemic were dead, cholera itself was not.

It continued to convulse epidemically, that is, it broke out in large though localized areas. The outbreak of cholera at El Korein, Egypt, in September 1947, is representative.

El Korein is on the Nile Delta close by the Sweet Water Canal, a fitting name for the line that supplies Suez' drinking water. September 1947 was a time of overcrowding there. Tens of thousands were gathered for a trade fair. Six thousand men were working on a heavy construction project. Three construction workers were the first stricken and news of their fall triggered another communicable disease which is often a companion of cholera: panic. The tens of thousands fled. Instead of escaping the disease, however, many took it wherever they went. They had already drunk water contaminated by the vibrio and it was working inside them. In a month 33,000 cases were reported in Egypt. Before the epidemic was squelched four months later, 20,472 were dead.

Occurrence in Hong Kong in 1966 is also representative of the world cholera situation today. In Hong Kong human waste is collected from buildings lacking plumbing, between midnight and six a.m., by female employees of the Urban Services Department. This chore is called Nightsoil Collection. It is an unpleasant, undesirable, but necessary job. It is the Crown Colony's first line of defense against cholera.

The nightsoil collectors empty each building's pails into collection trucks stopping at fixed points along a number of established routes, not unlike newspaper or mail routes. At the end of each route the wastes are loaded aboard barges which take it to storage tanks. After processing it is sold to farmers for fertilizer.

Samples are taken from each truck unloading at the barge point. If a sample proves positive, that is, shows cholera vibrio, the area from which it came is known. Backtracking to the specific house from which infection comes, and finding the person infected in it, is a simple matter.

On November 23, 1966 a 56-year-old vegetable farmer from Kowloon was admitted to a hospital. He was badly dehydrated and trembling in diarrhea spasms. Diagnosis: cholera.

That same day in Hong Kong several nightsoil loads were found to be contaminated with cholera vibrios. Nightsoil tests continued to prove positive for several subsequent days.

The obvious conclusion is incorrect, however; circumstances are not always what they appear to be. The Kowloon vegetable farmer had not carried cholera to Hong Kong, nor had he brought it home from there. He had not been outside Kowloon for a considerable period.

In Hong Kong the source was traced to five waterfront district houses billeting transient seamen. Public health workers sought and found 93 people who had been in the five houses on November 23 and after. Each was tested for vibrios and found negative. Further tests of excrement samples showed the disease had vanished overnight as dramatically as it had appeared.

The Kowloon case and the Hong Kong case of the same day were established as being unconnected and coincidental. No other cholera appeared in either Kowloon or Hong Kong. The farmer's case was the only one recorded that year in the Hong Kong-Kowloon area. The implications are clear, however. "Without nightsoil monitoring the existence of the infection on Hong Kong Island would not have been detected," said a report written by three Hong Kong health officers, "and if circumstances had been other than described above, cases of cholera could have started appearing in an unsuspecting community." This is carefully phrased official language which means that without the nightly tests, cholera epidemics very possibly would have blazed in Hong Kong and Kowloon.

Clear questions are raised by these two incidents also.

How had the first three Egyptian workers contracted the disease? No one ever learned.

How had the Kowloon farmer picked up his infection? No one ever learned that either. Where had the Hong Kong vibrios come from? The best answer anyone can give is then they arrived from outside in classic manner on a ship carrying infected seamen. This answer however, is still only hypothesis.

It is now easy to detect cholera. It is also an easily arrested disease. When treatment is properly applied, death is rare. Yet, for all science can do, science still cannot answer the puzzling questions concerning cholera, as it cannot concerning other diseases. When does it come and why?

Still newer perplexities appear to stub the epidemiologist's toe. Example: It was once believed that there were no long term cholera carriers. It was felt the carrier state was rare. Now suddenly it appears that there is an El Tor carrier state which can last 1,000 days. Immediate answers are elusive.

A statement in *The Epidemiology of Cholera in India* by A.J.H. Russell and E.R. Sundararajan (1928) still holds true:

> The association of higher relative humidity with high temperatures, accompanied by intermittent rains, forms the most favorable atmosphere for the development of the disease. The presence of endemic centers from which epidemics spring at short intervals is also a fact which must be accepted. No single factor, however, can be held responsible for the periodic waves of the disease . . . and it must be recognized that these waves are preceded by conditions too complex to admit of complete solution with the aid of available data. Individual susceptibility, foci of infection, favorable atmospheric conditions, fairs and festivals, carriers, insanitary habits, all play their part in a manner which defies analysis.

Cholera remains the confounding disease it has been for centuries.

* * *

After a rapid decline in cholera incidence and spread in the late 1950's, epidemic waves fanned out again from the endemic foci in Southeast Asia. Beginning in 1961, the El Tor strain invaded the western Pacific area. Recently, cholera has again set upon large areas in Asia proper, from the Caspian Sea to the Pacific Ocean. In December 1967 the World Health Organization stated "Four of manking's worst communicable diseases are on the increase." One was cholera.

Iran reported an outbreak of El Tr in 1965. So did Bahrein, and Uzbekistan, Iraq's turn came in 1966. In May 1966 Cambodia called upon various countries via WHO for several million doses of cholera vaccine to prevent an epidemic. In May 1967 Cambodia was vaccinating 500,000 persons at that time in the Battambang area. In July 1965 Afghanistan reported advent of cholera and requested a million vaccine doses from WHO.

Total reported world case load has been hovering at about 70,000 per year. Of those afflicted, more than 21,000 have been dying. Add to this additional unreported thousands.

There is once again a pandemic loose in the world.

To deal with it, WHO convened a Conference on International Cooperation in the Prevention of Cholera in Ankara, Turkey, in late February 1967. Eighteen countries attended and agreed that there are 11 major difficulties common to cholera control programs:

1—Protection of certain areas is almost impossible because of the increased speed of travel, expansion of tourism, migrant labor and nomad movements.

2—Inadequate sanitation of some ports, airports, bus and train stations, and layover spots on sea and land routes.

3—The difficulty of impressing the public with need for personal hygiene.

4—Difficulties always found in early detection of symptomless or mild infections, and especially in carrier detection.

5—Certain characteristics of *Vibrio cholerae* which deceive diagnosticians and render laboratory findings unreliable.

6—Difficulty encountered in transporting cases to distant treatment centers.

7—Failure to realize that only certain foods under certain circumstances and for limited time, may be effective cholera carriers.

8—Lack of bilateral and multilateral agreements on preparation, storage, shipment, and decontamination of perishable foods.

9—The unsubstantiated belief that cholera can be transmitted by goods, animals, and even mail.

10—Lack of enforcement of proper sanitary methods for disposal of sewage from ships, aircraft, trains, etcetera.

11—Incomplete and/or neglected disinfection of homes, public places, transportation facilities likely to be contaminated, and places where corpses are handled.

The participants also agreed that officials in infected areas must take rigorous precautions to prevent cholera's export. Eastern Mediterranean countries have significantly increased their cholera protection ability by practicing a "good neighbor" policy. They render prompt assistance to cholera-stricken nations by sending vaccines, drugs, infusion fluids, equipment, and physicians. WHO has contributed supplies, literature, information, individual consultants, and teams. It has also offered training courses and fellowships and has established a vaccine bank and a special account for cholera control.

The conference outlined four principles of cholera control:

1—Strengthen health services so that control can be enforced without interrupting life and ways of the country's people.

2—Promote sanitary improvements and general health education.

3—Concentrate efforts to wipe out old and new endemic foci.

4—Scrupulously apply the International Sanitary Regulations, avoiding both excessive and ineffective measures.

To implement these principles, the conference recommended:

1—Investigation of all enteric and diarrheal diseases.

2—Training of more medical, paramedical, and laboratory people.

3—Developing modern rehydration and other treatment facilities. The conference held this to be of paramount importance. Reason: Where such facilities are available and used promptly, mortality drops to less than one per cent.

4—Building sanitation facilities to keep pace with development of industry, urban areas, tourism, and trade.

5—Initiation of cooperative national and international research on viability of the El Tor vibrio in local food products, especially those which are prepared for export.

Finally, the conference stated that early and reliable reporting of all quarantinable diseases is a moral and legal obligation of every state.

*   *   *

Not all communicable disease problems are international and pandemic. Some are local and personal and tax the ingenuity and patience of the public health field worker. These people must anticipate the booby traps of local custom and practice. Sound public health projects can fail if field workers are not perceptive. A case in point:

The public well of one village in India was a filthy open pit. Women drew water by dropping in communal buckets attached to vines. Both buckets and vines were black with grime. It was custom among the women to simply drop them in the dirt after use. In this same dirt were leavings of people who had excreted in passing by. Well and buckets were likely sources of cholera and other waterborne disease.

A sanitation team told the villagers, "We'll build you a new well with a cover and pumps. We set only one condition."

"What is that?" the villagers asked.

"That you keep the cover locked so the women cannot use soiled buckets in the well. Anyone can draw water by pushing a button. The pumps will make it flow from outside spigots."

"Wonderful," the delighted villagers said, and the old well was walled, covered, and fitted with belt driven pumps. Most delighted of all were the women who would no longer have to haul heavy buckets.

A year passed.

A passing inspection party found the well doors broken open, the pumps in disuse, and the women once more dropping their old buckets on foul ropes to draw water. The well was as dirty and menacing as ever. The only difference was, now it had a cover.

Why had the villagers rejected the equipment which had once pleased them so? The answer was simple.

The people who planned and built the well completely forgot Hindu reverence for the cow as a holy animal. It was offensive to the villagers to use or eat anything from a cow.

The drive belts were made, as drive belts often are, of cowhide.

PROFILE OF CHOLERA:

Definition: A serious, acute infectious intestinal disease. It is bacterial and characterized by diarrhea, muscle cramps, and prostration.

Symptoms: Sudden onset. Vomiting. Profuse watery stool. Rapid and extensive dehydration. Physical collapse. Body becomes clammy with sweat. Temperature drops as low as 85°F (armpit reading).

Fatality: Rates run from five to 15 per cent in endemic cholera, up to 75 per cent in widespread epidemics.

Complications: Several possible in certain varieties of cholera, the severest complications being: anuria, bronchial pneumonia, gangrene of toes and fingers.

Infectious agent: Vibrio cholerae (called classic cholera) a short motile bacteria shaped like a comma or "S". *Vibrio cholerae* includes El Tor strain.

Occurrence: Classic *Vibro cholerae* is endemic in India and East Pakistan; epidemics burst forth from time to time. Cholera has been absent on epidemic scale from Western Hemisphere and Europe for several decades. Last recorded U.S. case was 1911, in New York City. El Tor strain is indistinguishable clinically and epidemiologically from classic cholera.

Reservoir: Man.

Infection Source: Feces and vomit discharge of patients, mostly. To a lesser degree, feces of persons either incubating or convalescing from the disease are also a source.

Transmission: Commonly, via contaminated water, less commonly by food. Later cases ordinarily are transmitted by direct contact, by foods contaminated by soiled hands or utensils, and by flies.

Portal of Infection: Alimentary tract only.

Incubation: From a few hours to five years; two or three days generally.

Communicability period: Classic cholera vibrios usually persist in feces for seven to 14 days, occasionally for as long as three months. As previously noted, however, El Tor type cholera can persist much longer. Carrier states lasting as long as 1,000 days have been observed in the Philippines.

Susceptibility: Is variable and related to nutritional state. People on poor diet are more susceptible than those on sound diet.

Resistance: Recovery from a clinical attack affords victim some short-term immunity. Artificial vaccine-induced immunity is of undetermined degree and short duration, six months at most.

Vaccine: Made from heat-killed cultures, administered subcutaneously in two or three doses, beginning with 0.5 cc and then 0.1 cc. Each dose contains about 8,000,000 organisms per cc.

Specific treatment: Rehydration is most important measure; it can mean the difference between dying and living. Promptly administer generous amounts of fluid and electrolyte, and other measures to prevent shock. Tetracyclines may prove valuable for reducing volume and duration of diarrhea and passing of vibrios.

Prevention: Here sanitation is paramount, that is, human waste disposal, water purification, milk pasteurization, fly control, enforcement of sanitary food handling measures. Also, vaccination of individual running risk of cholera.

Control:

1—Reporting of case or cases to local health officials is important. Report is universally required by International Sanitary Regulations.

2—Isolate patient or patients during communicable period, preferably in hospital.

3—Quarantine and observe (this is known in public health parlance as "surveillance") all persons contacting patients or patient for five days, longer if cholera vibrios appear in contacts' stool.

4—Search for unreported cases. Probe for sources of infection in polluted drinking water, contaminated foods.

Note: Vaccination of contacts after exposure is of little value; it will do no more than shield against subsequent or continued exposure.

Basic public health measures during epidemics:

1—Vaccinate exposed populations, despite cholera vaccine's uncertain worth.

2—Boil, chlorinate, or otherwise treat water used for drinking, bathing, and washing food utensils.

3—Seek out all infected persons. Set up temporary emergency facilities for isolation of patients and suspects. Detain those traveling to other localities for five days.

4—Watch over food and drink after cooking or boiling to prevent contamination by flies, other infected or carrier humans, et cetera.

International measures:

1—Government notifies WHO and neighbors of the first imported, first transferred, or first nonimported cholera case in any local area previously free of the disease.

2—Measures applicable to ships, aircraft, land transport arriving from cholera areas to put into effect. These are specified in International Sanitary Regulations, WHO, annotated edition, Geneva, 1966.

3—Many countries require travelers from a cholera country area to show a valid international cholera vaccination certificate. The certificate is valid from six days until six months after the first vaccination, six months after each revaccination.

THE PREVAILING EPIDEMIC.

"AH! YOU MAY LAUGH, MY BOY; BUT IT'S NO JOKE BEING FUNNY WITH THE INFLUENZA!"

A personal editorial comment on an 1847 influenza outbreak in England, by a cartoonist for Punch.

III INFLUENZA

". . . the new acquaintance."

Influenza literally means influence.

The word is Italian and was given as name to the disease some time during the 13th century. It referred to the effect the stars were imagined to have on man's health, as described by a passage from *The Chronicles of a Florentine Family, 1200-1470* by Ginevra Niccolini di Camugliano:

> Many important events were attributed to the influence of the stars: storms, earthquakes, famines and epidemics. If Florence was in the grip of an epidemic of colds, coughs and fevers, astrologers were consulted, and they declared that it was caused by the influence of an unusual conjunction of planets. This sickness, which kept recurring from to time in hard winters, came gradually to be known as "influenza."

In the 18th century the sickness was also known as *un influenza di freddo,* or an influence of cold wind, since it appeared mostly in winter. Dr. John Huxham of Plymouth (1692-1768) brought the word to the English language in papers written in 1743. Thus it has remained in the original Italian spelling ever since as influenza, or influence.

For such a disease, such a label is misleading. Influence by definition is a gentle word lacking violent connotations. Mildness is inherent in it. The disease itself perpetuates a myth of mildness; it displays qualities of mercy alien to other scourges; it is a disease characterized by aching and shaking rather than terrifying symptoms. It manifests itself with drowsy fever and a feeling the skin has shrunk several sizes, mere discomforts compared to the body-draining ravages of cholera. Mortality, even during epidemics sometimes, is generally low. In endemic times the public regards influenza with about as much horror as it does the common cold.

This influence, this influenza, is not a mild thing, however. It intimidates, wastes and decimates populations. During the past 25 centuries it has at times diverted the flow of events and buried more corpses than the medieval plagues.

With its major complications (bronchitis and pneumonia) it is the number six killer in the United States; more than 57,000 perished during the 1963 epidemic. Influenza breaks out somewhere in the United States in epidemic form every two or three years. There is no rest in between epidemics; influenza is endemic at all times, in winter more than in summer, but endemic 365 days a year.

Like cholera and the other perplexing communicable diseases, it wages guerrilla war; strike and retreat, strike and retreat, in predictable cycles.

Influenza is more befuddling than other communicables, however. It possess more gadfly qualities. Its origins are murkier and exits more dramatic. And, as a guerrilla enemy camouflages himself, influenza changes its form and appears as a baffling new disease.

Influenza wages its war in a particularly shifty guerrilla way. Influenza has no traditional home or endemic focus as cholera does in the Ganges Delta. It never enters a dormant state which would give both itself and mankind a breather. Influenza is always on the move; hence it is always breaking out somewhere at some time. It must feed upon itself to preserve itself. It must, as guerrillas must, march or die. It characteristically attacks separate localities simultaneously.

Other ugly things in influenza's epidemiological profile:

● The disease infiltrates the tightest quarantines. Not being endemic to one place, it can therefore be expected anywhere. Public health agencies cannot trap it if they do not know where to look for it. V.M. Zhdanov of the USSR Academy of Medical Sciences, writing in *The Role of Immunization in Communicable Disease Control* published by the World Health Organization in 1961, noted, ". . . influenza is perhaps the only truly global infection, knowing no state boundaries . . . influenza exists at the present moment as an infection of humanity as a whole."

● Mass vaccination is of limited effectiveness. Working immunity lasts a year at most. Yet, mass vaccination so far is the most effective defense, if a flu onslaught can be anticipated. Vaccination after outbreak is of little, if any, value.

● Influenza is not one enemy, it is three. Research workers have isolated three main groups of the virus: A, B, and C. Within A and B are some 1,500 different strains or subgroups. The diversity complicates immunization; to be effective, vaccine must be manufactured from the same infective organisms it is to fight.

● There is no known specific medication for influenza.

This cheerless bill of particulars lists one encouraging item, namely, influenza is easy to identify. It betrays its own arrival by its very virulence. To an epidemiologist any outbreak of acute, infectious, respiratory viral infection which strikes down many people in several localities at once within a few days is flu.

※　　※　　※

By virtue of its evasion of permanent immunization influenza has been termed "the last of the unconquered scourges," a label many public health people hold to be overblown. The WHO position is, no disease can be called "the last unconquerable" while other abhorrences (such as onchocerciasis, blinding millions of Africans) still rage.

Flu has been known in the past by less sweeping names. Italians also spoke of their influence of cold wind as the "malignant catarrh." Seventeenth century Englishmen called influenza the "gentle correction," "the grip," and the "jolly rant," this last being a puzzle because it literally means merry noisemaking.

The English also termed influenza "the new acquaintance" in misbelief that it was a new disease each time it reappeared. They are not to be chided for their ignorance. They inherited little from their predecessors to teach them differently.

A passage in *Corpus Hippocraticum* describes an affliction which drove an Athenian army from the field in 412 B.C. The affliction is felt to have been flu but the description is neither clinically perfect enough nor clinically complete enough to say that it was for sure.

Ancient disease descriptions were more reliable than ancient treatments, however. There were several major schools of medical thought in Greece in the fifth and fourth centuries B.C. Influenza, cancer, fractures, all injuries and afflictions, were treated in ways prescribed by one school or another, depending upon the patient's preference.

Most powerful and popular among Greeks was the Aesculapian Cult, a religious group practicing "temple medicine." This was faith healing containing recognizable elements of psychotherapy. The godhead of the cult was Aesculapius. In Greek mythology Aesculapius is the son of the nymph Coronis who was ordered slain by Apollo. Aesculapius studied healing arts under Chiron the centaur, as legend goes, and performed medical miracles for which he was made a god with place and privileges on Mount Olympus. He was worshipped throughout Greece as a healer.

The sick flocked to the temples of Aesculapius to "incubate," that is, sleep beside the god's statute (generally of marble and gold). They prayed Aesculapius and his daughters Hygeia and Panacea would appear in their dreams and effect miraculous cures.

Many who drowsed ill awakened well, claiming Aesculapius had indeed cured them. Some told of Aesculapius prescribing herbs. Others described wondrous surgery. Absence of scars and wounds made the surgery still more wondrous. Today such illnesses and their relief are studied as psychosomatic medicine; the parallel is plain.

Ancient Roman medicine was many things. It was often magical; bronze mirrors engraved with demons were hung to drive off sickness. It was often preventive; medical students were barred from brothels by law so they would not contract social diseases. It was often absurd. Highly recommended for various ailments were cabbage cures; especially baths in urine of persons who ate cabbage. The wife of the Roman statesman Cato (234-149 B. C.) died in such a bath.

A mixture of turtle blood, camel brains, and crocodile excrement was popular as aspirin is today for treating many fevers and ailments.

These ancient unpleasantries were probably used to cure influenza and other diseases. They were of no value of course.

With time, influenza was seen as a truly separate disease itself rather than merely symptom or concomitant of others. The first outbreak which can be reasonably identified as influenza alone was that of "a certain evil and unheard of cough" in 1173. The cough sickened thousands of Italians, Germans and Englishmen; death rates are not known.

Outbreaks of something beleaguered 15th century Europeans, though records are not positive enough to say for sure that it was influenza. 1510 is the year the disease was finally awarded title of a full-blown pestilence, though it was not often called by its Italian name, influenza. The outbreak which shook Europe and the Middle East in 1580 is considered the first influenza pandemic of record. This "separate disease" realization represented advanced thinking of those times; on the other hand treatment remained in a retarded state.

During pestilence such as influenza, hard cases who refused to recover were sometimes bound up together on the cathedral floors, dozens at a time. They were left in their own filth until they decided to permit faith healing to cure them, or until they died.

The English "sweating sickness" was probably influenza, though some historians say absence of coughing, pneumonia complications and quick following waves spell out typhus. The "sweat" was also another of the classic epidemic mysteries. It came on like a landslide in 1485. After five epidemics it vanished as blown dust in 1552.

The English sweat came to London with soldiers marching from the Battle of Bosworth Field in 1485, the final clash of the Wars of the Roses. Its epidemiology is dark; where did the soldiers themselves contract it? No no knows.

In London it killed the lord mayor. Then it killed his successor and six aldermen. It struck the waterfront, bedding so many sailors that England's men o' war could not sail on English Channel patrol. Henry VII (1457-1509) postponed his coronation because of it in 1485. In some rural districts it killed half the population.

It crossed the channel and sickened 15,000 in Augsburg, Germany, in five days. In another German city, Goettingen, it killed at such rates that burial parties could not keep up with the work; they buried eight corpses in each grave. The sweat ambushed Turks besieging Vienna in 1529 and is given as cause for their subsequent withdrawal.

The English sweat's manner of killing was ugly. Manifestations were pounding heart, vomiting, and incendiary fever which made a man feel that all the world's water could not cool him. Death was blitzkrieg swift. Victims went in a day, some within a few hours. Farmers kissed their wives goodbye in the morning and food them dead at noon.

During five epidemics between 1485 and 1552 the sweat felled millions. An attack of sweat probably bestowed little or no natural immunity; this is suspected because thousands suffered several successive bouts.

To treat the English sweat both legitimate doctors and quacks prescribed tobacco extracts, lime juice (which in truth did help seamen with scurvy), emetics, purgatives, physics. They bled their patients and probably hastened their deaths; persons so ill could not afford loss of blood.

Little could be done to stop influenza. Indeed, until isolation of the causative organism in 1933, treatment was a hit or miss proposition.

One reason was that when Rome fell, the body of sensible pharmacology and knowledge of medication fell with it. For well over 1,000 years the magical approach to medicine was taken by most. Diseases generally were viewed as punishments imposed by God upon wicked mankind. St. Augustine (?-651) in the fifth century established a creed observed until the 19th century: "All diseases of Christians are to be ascribed to demons."

Englishmen of lesser faith held flu to be caused by "effervescence of blood in spring."

As all pestilence does, influenza also traveled the trade routes, and in 1647, ships sailing from Spain brought it to the New World. Its arrival represents one of the few occasions in centuries of shaky fact on which definite dates, sources, and transmission lines can be identified. The ships came from Valencia. The disease was present at embarkation. Crews and passengers contracted it there, passed it back and forth to one another on the voyage, and brought it in with them. In America the disease was called the "Spanish Influence."

How often did influenza flare up during the next 150 years? This is difficult to answer. It almost certainly reappeared often. The notion that lice had some connection with disease was taking hold, for example, but the measures to curb lice were both comic and saddening. To attract and kill the creatures fashionable men and women placed sponges soaked in honey and vinegar under their wigs.

There is no mistaking the outbreaks of 1645, 1743, and 1782; they were definitely influenza.

In Rome, 1743, more than 80,000 collapsed. Five hundred died in a single day. Several coffin shops closed because they could not fill so many orders.

The 1782 outburst was pandemic, touching Europe, China, and America. A prior incident in 1780 involving the British East India Company ship *Atlas* demonstrated the ways such pandemics spread in seemingly indiscriminate, directionless leaps.

Atlas was sailing from Malacca to Canton. In mid-China Sea the crew came down with influenza almost to a man. Yet, there had been no contagion in Malacca during *Atlas'* call there earlier. Where had the flu come from? Crewmen were baffled.

They were astonished when they arrived in Canton. There they learned an influenza outbreak has lashed this city some weeks earlier. It coincided in time with the one aboard their own ship.

How had the same disease arrived before them?

It hadn't. The answer is influenza's unique ability to appear in several places simultaneously, seemingly without connection. It is not necessarily a chain reaction disease.

As shipping volume increased in this century, as faster ships were built, the mystery of "preceding influenza" was noted frequently and marveled at. Decades passed before the hopscotch nature of this disease was understood.

English author Daniel Defoe (1660-1731) noted in his *Journal of the Plague Year* that the pestilence "despised all medicine" employed to defeat it. So did its comrade influenza.

Of all the hardships suffered by American revolutionary troops wintering at Valley Forge in 1777-78, "the influence" was one of the harshest. One army doctor, unable to do anything about it, quoted Defoe's sentiment toward plague: "I looked upon this dismal time to be a particular season of divine vengeance."

An early American (and an unlikely one) concerned with flu was Noah Webster, the dictionary man (1758-1843). He determined that there had been 44 epidemics since 1174 and added his own wild hunch to the vast store of folklore on causes. He wrote:

> The causes most probably exist in the elements, fire, air, and water for we know of no other medium by which diseases can be communicated to whole communities of people.

His feelings toward it were Italian; to Webster influenza was "evidently the effect of some insensible qualities of the atmosphere . . . and electrical quality."

In the 19th century pandemics occurred in 1830, 1837, 1847. This last one appeared to flail London in a particularly vicious manner. The high figures were probably due to a more efficient recording system which took in more victim statistics, however, rather than any special local severity.

Dr. Theophilus Thompson of London observed in his milestone *Annals of Influenza* published in 1852: "Influenza does not, like plague, desert for ages a country which it has once afflicted, nor is it accustomed, like the sweating sickness, in any marked manner to limit its attack to particular nations, or race of mankind. There is grandeur in its constancy and immutability superior to the influence of the national habits . . ." The statement is important because it was one of the few accurate observations on the spread of influenza made by anyone up to that time.

Then, for four decades, no flu occurred in western Europe and only in localized epidemics elsewhere, in Russia for example.

The 40 flu-free years ended with the pandemic of 1890, as it is called. This pandemic was actually four: 1889, 1891, 1892, and 1893. It was called "Chinese Distemper," another spurious labeling which contributed so much to anti-Chinese sentiment in the United States. Medical men believed this outbreak was somehow caused by or brought by the dust clouds blown up from the parched banks of the Yellow River in drought. They had no reason to believe so; there was no proof.

There was also a suggestion the pandemic began in a "virus reservoir" built up in Siberia during epidemics there in 1886 and 1887. There is no evidence such a reservoir existed. Nonetheless, the 1890 pandemic was also known as "Russian Influenza" in many areas. Floating volcanic ash from the eruption of Mt. Krakatoa off Sumatra in 1883 was also blamed.

The disease seemed to largely disappear for the next 25 years; actually it really hadn't. England and Wales had been almost completely free of influenza until 1890. From 1890 onward, however, the disease was always present. The annual death rate topped pre-1890 levels until it fell again in 1948. There was a tendency in the western world to put aside thoughts of epidemics early in the 20th century. For one reason, there was something else of greater concern to Europe and the Americas. A world war was shaping up in the Balkans.

*   *   *

1918.
In the spring of this year, influenza appeared at Fort Riley,

Kansas, among troops mustered for shipment to the trenches of France. There were other outbreaks too. Simultaneously it showed up at various other military installations and localities in the United States. That summer, influenza appeared in Europe wherever American troops landed. These attacks were gentle, nothing compared to the drama of the war itself. Collectively they were called "the mild summer wave."

They were not mild attacks. Though numbers of victims were low, deaths were high. In England the flu seemed to leap right into pneumonia complications. Throughout Europe, on both sides of the war fronts, the same situation prevailed; incidence low, mortality high. But for the war, the threat of an impending worldwide horror would probably have been seen clearly and immediately.

This time the disease was called many things: The "Flanders grippe" by men serving in Flanders, "Chungking fever" in parts of France where Chinese labor had dug trenches, "wrestler's fever" by the Japanese Imperial Navy, and "Blitz Katarrh" by German troops coughing and spitting blood in their trenches.

The name it was called most was an old one: "Spanish Influenza." One French soldier wrote to his family saying the name sounded like a harmless Spanish dance. Why Spain became bearer of the stigma again is not clear. King Alfonso XIII (1886-1941) contracted it and this is suggested as one possible reason for the Spanish label.

Responsible officials insisted on ignoring the threat as late as September 1918. Despite a mounting record of cases on his desk, New York City's health commissioner said, "The city is in no danger of an epidemic." A few days later there were 30 more, all seamen from the Brooklyn Navy Yard, all suffering influenza.

The summer wave was followed by a second wave in November 1918 and a third in March 1919.

When the casualty figures started coming in, complacency ended. No more could a health commissioner ignore facts and say his city was in no danger. Influenza was flooding the earth and not even the term pandemic was broad enough to describe the damage it was doing.

This influenza was one of the most destructive holocausts in all history to this present time. Only the great medieval plagues outmatch it in virulence and deadliness. They were worse and took as many victims in Europe alone.

● Flu (and its pneumonic complications) took 20,000,000 lives by conservative estimate. It sickened 50 times this number, more than a billion.

● 50 per cent of the dead were between ages 20 and 40, the world's most vital and productive population group.

● India was brutalized more than any other country. Here 12,500,000 are said to have perished, or four per cent of the total population.

● In the United States 20,000,000 fell ill. More than 500,000 of these died.

● Flu touched everywhere in the world except the Tristan de Cunha Islands in the South Atlantic Ocean. Coast Guard parties discovered entire Eskimo villages of dead in remote Alaskan areas.

Flu claimed more lives than the four years of world war did; total war dead numbered 8,538,000.

Again the tragedies of masses are illustrated by the agony of individuals. For example:

Two Nova Scotia nurses who volunteered to nurse patients in Boston contracted flu themselves, died within hours of each other, and were buried together.

Many Samoans died, not from the disease, but from starvation. Nine in ten were sick and too weak to prepare and apportion emergency rations sent to them.

In Chicago, a laborer whose wife and four children were terminal flu cases shouted from his house, "I'll cure them my own way!" Then he slit their throats.

Among the farfetched explanations offered for the pandemic in the U.S. were: Sugar deficiency caused by wartime rationing, eating fish infected with influenza germs spread underwater by German submarines, dust from books donated to soldiers.

Some equally farfetched cure suggestions were:

Going naked to permit the skin to breathe, sprinkling sulfur in one's shoes, and boiling large pots of red peppers in homes and public buildings.

In October 1918 more than 40,000 reeled about Omaha with the "three-day fever." Hog prices in this city dropped to 17 cents per pound wholesale because people avoided markets as they did all public places. The American Expeditionary Force in France counted 70,000 cases in field hospitals. AEF fatalities were running an average 32 per cent, as high as 80 per cent in some units. More than 14,000 English died of influenza complications during the first week of November.

People did their best and worst in coping with the scourge.

One of the hardest workers at New York City's Henry Street Settlement was a prostitute.

In Atlanta, Georgia, landlords evicted stricken tenants.

Nomadic Finns locked their sick in unheated communal huts and fed them by shoving reindeer milk and meat under the doors. It seemed to be a correct thing to do, cruel as it sounds. Many recovered.

Three San Francisco men wearing the popular white protective masks robbed a taxi driver and dumped him from his cab.

The pestilence, or a strain of it, raged among farm and jungle animals. In South Africa tens of thousands of baboon corpses dotted the veldt. They apparently had no resistance to flu.

Then. . . . Almost as quickly as it had come on, the influenza pandemic subsided in spring 1919, a happy accompaniment to the first spring of world peace in almost five years.

Its departure reflected the grand style of the pandemics, that is, it was mysterious and unfathomable.

The mystery prevails to this day. No one knows the etiology of Spanish Influenza. No one knows where it came from, or where it went. Indeed, no one knows whether the particular virus even exists any longer because it has never, ever been seen again.

*   *   *

There were other epidemics in 1922, 1927, 1929. None showed the ferocity or spread of 1918-19, but all possessed the same air of mystery. The most research workers could agree upon concerning origin during this decade was:

Influenza was caused by its own particular organism, a microscopic, filterable virus, as yet unidentified and undescribed.

The most anyone could say of immunity after infection was:

Protection, if any, was of undetermined scope and duration.

Measures for dealing with it were still those of the 17th century pandemic: alcohol rubs to lower temperatures, aspirin, quinine, hot soup, pneumonia jackets. There were no moves ahead, for no one in research or practical medicine knew where to go.

The first major breakthrough in influenza etiology came in 1933 at the National Institute for Medical Research in London. In that year, three scientists isolated the first human influenza virus, called Type A, from throat washings of victims of a then current outbreak. As photographed by the electron microscope it appears as a fluffy white ball, so tiny 15,000,000 can fit on a typewritten period without touching one another. There is no doubt that type A alone, without bacterial accompaniment, has caused most epidemics and pandemics since its discovery. Reasons for its appearance is, as always, still murky.

In 1934 Dr. Thomas Francis, Jr. painstakingly isolated an A type strain or subtype called PR-8 during research at the University of Michigan. PR-8 is the classic A strain that plagues the United States during certain periods.

Type A was believed to be the only type of influenza to exist until the same Dr. Francis isolated the first strains of a type known as B in 1940.

General characteristics of type B are similar to those of type A. It is more difficult to infect experimental animals with B, however. Also, infection by one grants no immunity to the other; in this respect they are different diseases.

In 1943 the first promising practical flu vaccine was tested by the U.S. Army's Commission on Acute Respiratory Diseases. This panel was charged with finding ways to protect servicemen from repetition of the 1918-1919 horror show.

The vaccine was made of both A and B types suspended in sodium chloride solution and killed by formalin. This last is wood alcohol with 40 per cent formaldehyde content. Dosage was one cubic centimeter administered subcutaneously.

The test involved two groups, one vaccinated, one unvaccinated, with thousands of soldiers in each. Only 2.2 per cent of the vaccinated group contracted type A during a subsequent outbreak. In the unvaccinated group 7.11 per cent were striken.

The entire U.S. Army was vaccinated in 1945. During a type B wave that winter, only one per cent of the vaccinated men caught the infection. Among the unvaccinated service groups incidence was 10 to 13 per cent.

And vaccination is as far as things have come since then.

True, there is work in progress leading toward broad spectrum vaccines that will afford immunity to many flu strains for at least five years. The Soviet Union ran large scale live vaccine tests in 1965-66 on persons over 12 in Smolensk and Jarcevo with promising results. Continuing studies offer up new insights into immunity yearly.

True, influenza epidemics can be predicted; the frequency seems to be every two to three years in North America according to the International Influenza Center for the Americas, in Atlanta, Georgia.

And true, the World Influenza Center in London, watches and watches and watches to point of boredom all the globe's flu epidemics for viral changes. If a variation is emerging, the center will help develop new vaccines.

Yet a cure is still to come; holes still exist in the influenza technology. In many ways the disease is only less the mystery and less the enemy it was in 1918-19. It is still an enemy. New outbreaks occur to trouble man and new strains appear to further baffle him.

There were moderate epidemics in England and Wales in 1949, 1951, 1953. In 1957 a new type A strain, labeled "Asian Flu" because it first appeared in China, galloped across Southeast Asia, Africa, the Middle East, Europe and the Americas. In the United States it gave fevers to more than half the population and killed 19,000 more than usually die in a year from influenza and pneumonia.

In 1960 a million in and around Los Angeles gagged and sweated under a "new" disease they called by the intimidating name "Q Flu." This was nothing new. It was the same Asian flu that was wasting the rest of the country.

In December 1967 the National Communicable Disease Center of the U.S. Department of Health, Education, and Welfare said, "Influenza or similar illnesses continued to strike sections of the Northeast, Middle West, and deep South." More than 7,000 in one Alabama county were driven to doctors by the disease in one week.

In New York City health authorities expected one in every ten to fall prey to "the Asian bug" between December 1 and March 1, or, 1,000,000 people.

People tempered anxiety by gallows humor as they have done in crisis for centuries. In one instance it took verse form. A jingle of undetermined authorship recited often was in the style and meter of the "Roses are red, violets are blue" school:

Noses are red;
Eyelids are too.
One out of ten
New Yorkers have flu.

It was no joking matter, however. As influenza spread, death rates shot up. Typically, classic pneumonia complications were responsible, not flu itself. Pneumonia death figures for the 1967-68 winter were 20 per cent higher than those for 1966-67.

The frustrations of dealing with influenza's guerrilla evasiveness have been summed up by some unnamed WHO official:

"It's like going out to look for a man you've been told is three feet high to beat bloody hell out of him only to find he's now grown to eight feet and is beating bloody hell out of you."

PROFILE OF INFLUENZA:

Definition: Acute respiratory infection.

Symptoms: Abrupt onset. High fevers to 103° F. Sudden chills. Muscular pain. Coughing without expectoration. Prostration. Less frequent symptoms: Diarrhea. Gastrointestinal pain. In later stages: head cold, sore throat, nose bleeds sometimes develop. Blood pressure drops.

Influenza is a self limiting ailment; without treatment it runs definite course and ends within limited time. Recovery time is two to seven days.

Fatality: Rates low during nonepidemic periods, high during epidemics. *Important:* High epidemic incidence is a clear diagnostic signpost. Large case numbers are often first clues to flu identity. Single cases are difficult to identify. Small outbreaks can rapidly become epidemic.

Complications: If any, they are often bacterial pneumonia. Often fatal.

Infectious agent: Virus. Two types have been recognized since 1930's: Influenza A and influenza B. An influenza C is known but observed only sporadically. A and B subtypes affect men and animals. 1,500 A strains (different from subtypes) have been identified.

Subtype replacement is an unexplained phenomenon. Periodically a new subtype, never observed before appears. Current subtype vanishes causing no further flu in man. Current working A virus subtype A2 or "Asian Flu" has caused all A virus epidemics since 1957.

Occurrence: During epidemics 15-40 per cent of nonimmunized are stricken. Epidemics are cyclic. Influenza A strikes U.S. every two to three years, influenza B every four to six. In temperate climates flu is most prevalent in winter and spring, can come any season in tropics. Influenza also sickens swine, horses, other animals. "Swine flu" is suggested as 1918-19 pandemic cause.

Reservoir: Man.

Infection source: Mouth and nose discharges of infected persons.

Transmission: Direct contact such as kissing. Indirect contact via clothing or articles contaminated by fresh discharges. Flu is also possibly airborne.

Portal of infection: Nose, mouth.

Incubation: One to four days.

Communicability period: No more than three days from clinical onset.

Susceptibility: Universal. All ages, both sexes. Most vulnerable appear to be children about ten years old and young adults in 20s. Most likely to die of it are the elderly and patients already suffering cardiac, renal, pulmonary, and metabolic diseases.

Resistance: Infection grants immunity of undetermined length (perhaps several years) to infecting virus only. Repeated infection broadens immunity base.

Specific treatment: None. Sulfonamides and antibiotics have no effect on simple cases, are useful only in treating bacterial complications.

Prevention: Vaccinate persons running high risk of infection, those performing essential public services, those in high death risk brackets. (See: Susceptibility above.) Vaccinate before anticipated epidemics. Immunization after contact is valueless. Routine immunization of whole populations not recommended.

Control: Report all flu-like outbreaks to health authorities. Reporting is obligatory throughout U.S., not necessary in individual cases.

Isolate patients, primarily for patients' comfort. Quarantine, however, is generally ineffective.

Basic public health measures during epidemics Very few except to:

1—Anticipate outbreaks. Warn and rewarn public.

2—Report prevailing influenza type and outbreak patterns to state and national health authorities. Good reporting is essential to control.

3—Discourage public gatherings. Leave schools open. Closing schools has no proven value.

International measures:

1—Report epidemic to WHO. Identify virus type and subtype if possible. Describe epidemiologic and antigenic characteristics.

2—Send throat washings (term for discharge samples) and blood specimens for virus identification to one of 78 WHO laboratories in 53 countries. This laboratory network is headed by two international centers:

World Influenza Center
National Institute for Medical Research
London, England

International Influenza Center for the Americas
Communicable Disease Center
U.S. Public Health Service
Atlanta, Georgia
USA

3—Continue information exchange with WHO. Information is vital. With it, other areas yet untouched can anticipate epidemics and prepare. Example: Should some new subtype appear, well-informed producers can turn out new vaccine in time for the second round of the epidemic.

The legion of the damned. By their leper's cloaks and hats ordinary men knew them; they shrank from lepers and refused them comfort of neither kind word or dry roof. Lepers had little choice often but to roam in bands, begging a livelihood from town to town.

Vischer, 1608.

IV LEPROSY

". . . a disease, not a disgrace. . . ."

Leprosy is also called Hansen's Disease, after Gerhard Henrik Armauer Hansen (1841-1912). This imaginative Norwegian bacteriologist in 1871 determined by microscopic examination of biopsy sections that *Mycobacterium leprae*, a rod-shaped bacillus, causes the disease.

In all history there has been no more torturous pestilence than leprosy. It cripples, disfigures, and blinds. It is chronic, contagious, and until recently nearly impossible to treat or cure. It changes faces; people grow to resemble lions. It anesthetizes sense of touch; victims burn and mutilate themselves accidentally for they no longer feel pain. It brings on grotesque changes in the voice. It seldom kills by itself; it saps the body and opens way for other diseases to enter and do the killing. It progresses slowly and can bedevil sufferers for years.

True, all pestilences deal misery in large measure, so why then is leprosy the most torturous of all for its victims?

In addition to physical destruction the disease also brings the boundless abuse and loathing of others as no other disease does. The very word leprosy arouses horror; it is reasonable to say it is as much a disease of well minds as of sick bodies.

Medical historians agree that this loathing springs from the dread which God conveyed to the Israelites through the person of the Prophet Moses about 1,300 B.C., in the Sinai Desert after the flight from Egypt:

> And the Lord spake unto Moses and Aaron, saying,
> When a man shall have in the skin of his flesh a rising, a scab, or bright spot, and it be in the skin of his flesh like the plague of leprosy; then he shall be brought unto Aaron the priest. . . .
> And the priest shall look on the plague in the skin of the flesh: and when . . . the plague in sight be deeper than the skin of his flesh, it is a plague of

leprosy: and the priest shall . . . pronounce him
unclean.

—Leviticus, chapter 13.

The horror was further compounded by the harshness of the
God-given rules for handling leprosy victims. As further chronicled in Leviticus, the third book of the Old Testament, also
called the Third Book of Moses:

And the leper in whom the plague is, his clothes
shall be rent, and his head bare, and he shall put a
covering on his upper lip, and shall cry, Unclean,
unclean.

And the days wherein the plague shall be in him he
shall be defiled; he is unclean; he shall dwell alone;
without the camp shall his habitation be.

Still more fuel for prejudice was supplied by the measures
prescribed by priests cleansing the houses of those afflicted:

. . . if the plague be spread in the house, it is a
fretting leprosy . . . it is unclean.

And he [the priest] shall break down the house, the
stones of it, and the timber thereof, and all the mortar
of the houses and he shall carry them forth out of the
city into an unclean place.

As related by the unknown writers of Leviticus, the Lord also
describes some of the torturous symptoms of leprosy. He speaks
to Moses and Aaron of a raw flesh condition likely to be per-
forated ulcers. He describes skin patches resembling parchment.
He alludes to deformity of the feet. Ancient disease descriptions
are seldom so clinically close to the mark; a doctor today
will recognize leprosy in them.

If Divine word did not prejudice the community against the
leprosy sufferer, talks of wrathful Divine deed did. Chapter 12
of The Book of Numbers tells hows the ". . . anger of the
Lord was kindled . . ." because Moses' sister Miriam ". . .
spake against Moses because of the Ethiopian woman he had
married. . . ."

As punishment for gossiping and reviling the Lord made
Miriam ". . . leprous, white as snow. . . ."

The Hebrews probably first experienced leprosy in the land
which was the source of so much other grief for them: Egypt.

This may well account for their great fear of it. Egypt is one place in which leprosy was almost certainly endemic millenia before the Christ's birth.

As the Israelites migrated across the globe they brought their horror of leprosy with them. Wherever they passed they left some of it behind; here the belief in it as a Divine punishment, there the notion of leprosy people as filth, somewhere else the conviction the disease is forever uncurable. The horror took root, grew, flourished over the centuries, and in many minds and places still prevails.

Ancient India, Japan, and China knew leprosy. The Chinese described it as "Dragon Maggot Disease."

The lore-rich 4,000-year-old Ebers Papyrus, encyclopedia of so much medicine of antiquity, mentions a persistent eruptive disease probably leprosy. The reliable papyrus also proposes a remedy: "To drive away leprous spots on the skin, cook onions in sea salt and urine and apply as a poultice."

The Hebrews held no monopoly on detailed views and treatments. Leprosy is mentioned in the *Vedas* of India, probably written two centuries after Moses received the harsh leprosy mandates in Sinai. There are four *Vedas*. The word veda stands for knowledge or sacred lore. Early Indians believed the *Vedas* were revealed by Brahman, first member of the Hindu trinity and creator of the world, and given to holy men who passed them on to the masses by word of mouth. Similarity between Vedic legend and the Levitical account of the Lord instructing Moses is apparent. The *Vedas* are among the earliest Indian writings.

As described in the Vedic books, leprosy is symptomized by light spots seen easily on sunbronzed skin. A certain incantation, addressed by priests to an unidentified dark plant is the recommended cure:

> The leprosy and the gray spots drive away from
> here—may thy native color settle upon thee—the white
> spots cause to fly away! . . . The leprosy which has
> originated in the bones, and that which has originated
> in the body and upon the skin, the white mark begot-
> ten of corruption, I have destroyed with my charm.

A Hebrew word for skin scaling diseases was *zaraath*, but some historians feel this covered a gamut of conditions including psoriasis and ringworm but not leprosy.

The first known persecution of victims of this disease was ordered in Egypt by Pharoah Ramses II who reigned from 1292-1225 B.C. His soldiers drove more than 80,000 leprous persons into Sahara Desert compounds. How long they survived sun and thirst is not known to us, or, whether any survived at all.

*   *   *

It is assumed but cannot be said positively that the disease fanned out from Egypt sometime during this 1,200 to 1,000 years before Christ. As it did so the Israelites carried word of its horror.

Leprosy preferred the East. Between 1100 B.C. and 900 B.C. it became as common to all Asia as hunger. The West, for reasons yet undetermined, was not inviting to the *Mycobacterium leprae*.

It is probable that leprosy had a foothold in Europe by the fourth pre-Christian century, however. The Greeks had a word for it: *lepra*, meaning "scaly," the Greek equivalent of the Hebrew *zaraath*. Aristotle and Hippocrates both observed an affliction which was possibly leprosy and identified as *lepra*. The Greeks a few centuries later were it by its Roman nickname *elephantiasis graecorum*, or the Greek swelling.

How leprosy entered Europe proper:

As they were with plague and typhus, traveling armies were once more at fault. Leprosy came in as a camp follower of the Roman legions of Gnaeus Pompey (106-48 B.C.), esteemed general of Julius Caesar (100?-44 B.C.). The legions were returning, treasure laden and smug with glory, from Asia Minor in 62 B.C.

At Rome they passed it to other units. In time these units carried the disease to outposts in Gaul, Spain, Germany, and Britain.

The Romans were as indifferent to this disease as they were to an enemy. They certainly held none of the Eastern Mediterranean horror of it when it first appeared among homecoming troops.

One who did take it seriously was a worldly, erudite physician, known to us as Aretaeus of Cappadocia. He appears to have appreciated leprosy as something serious, infectious, debilitating, deforming, and deadly. It appears also that Aretaeus had public spirit; he set out to enlighten Rome concerning the disease locally called *elephas*, reference again to the sufferer's frequent swelling.

In late second century A.D. this man applied his gift for description to the problem and produced one of the first recognizable clinical descriptions of the disease. Its importance rests not in its primacy but its content. It is a sober profile which paints leprosy's frightful detail without attempt to frighten. It reads, in part:

> The disease named elephas and the animal named elephant have many properties in common. Formerly this affection was called leontiasis on account of the resemblance between the disease and the lion, produced by the appearance of the lower part of the forehead . . . it is filthy and dreadful to behold, in all respects like the wild animal, the elephant. Lurking among the bowels, like a concealed fire, it smoulders there . . . [then] blazes forth. . . ."

Following this description of lengthy incubation, Aretaeus then describes symptoms still recognized: stinking breath, tumors, dying and falling hair, distortion of nose and ears "resembling the elephant." Aretaeus then takes up the one manifestation of leprosy most repugnant to the beholder:

> . . . members of the patient will die, so as to drop off, such as the nose, the fingers, the feet, the privy parts and the whole hands; for the ailment does not prove fatal, so as to relieve the patient from a foul life and dreadful sufferings. . . .

Aretaeus noted leprosy's communicable nature and recommended isolation of victims in Rome's nearby mountains where they could be cared for and fed, out of contact with others. Some Romans followed this suggestion, but with less than compassion. They left their sick on the mountainsides without food or clothing to die, in the manner in which primitive man rid himself of unwanted children and old people.

Rome fell. The following medieval centuries, so reasonless, so intimidated by church and fear of God, were ideal times for lepraphobia to flourish. One of the things Europe acquired along with the Bible was the Biblical disgust toward leprosy and conviction that victims were either tested or punished by God.

No other view would have been possible. Suffering of some kind was accepted by all as a portion of divine punishment for sin present and original. For centuries Christians were constantly warned of the unholiness of seeking any but divine cure. Concerning illness, use of herbs and nostrums for everyday disorders was approved, but "To buy drugs," said the French ecclesiastic St. Bernard of Clairvaux (1091-1153) "to consult physicians, to take medicine befits not religion and is contrary to purity."

One God for kings, another for lepers. Powers of miraculous cure were attributed to the relics of St. Walpurga (?-779), housed in the cathedral at Eichstadt, Germany. Their healing touch was granted readily to nobles, but denied to lepers dying outside the church, as depicted by Flemish painter Barend van Orley (1491?-1542).   Musée d'Anvers.

Acceptance of the leprosy sufferers' lot then was enthusiastic, particularly by those who did not have leprosy. In 583 there was convened the Council of Lyon. This was the first weighty gathering of clergy ever in France. The attending clerics considered various matters, among them, ways of making the lives of leprosy sufferers holier though harsher. They decreed that they must henceforth associate only with other sufferers. Those who disobeyed were executed.

They were. And, in many ways, so were those who did obey.

In 644 in Lombardy every person showing leprosy symptoms was seized in a manner resembling the Nazi German roundoups of Jews for shipment to the concentration camps during World War Two. They were locked inside quarters outside Milan and there left to live out their lives. For most this was death. For food they had to depend upon friends and family; such unfortunates received little support from either.

Among those so persecuted throughout medieval centuries, and in all parts of the world were many who did not have leprosy at all. Scabies resembles leprosy. So does psoriasis and syphilis and a number of other ailments with eruption and/or swelling among their characteristics.

Leprosy madness served the greedy and the vengeful. Many a man cancelled his debt to another by circulating whispers that his benefactor's face inflamed by mere acne was "unclean." Men bearing grudges drove their enemies into exile simply by charging their dry skin was leprous skin.

Those not incarcerated were not left to suffer in peace and anonymity. It was not enough that their bursting skins and fragmenting limbs identified them as unclean; society demanded they don clothing by which all could know, shame, and shun them.

There evolved a uniform which, with minor regional variations, was common to all Europe: a black cloak with two white patches on the chest, a tall soft hat with a white patch or a white head shroud. Those whose faces were devastated wore masks so as not to disgust the public at large. Few of the public at larger ever came close enough to see their faces; all leprotics carried rattles or bells to warn of their presence.

A savage code of behavior was written for them; violations resulted in beatings or burnings. In the market place they pointed to purchases with a stick; with the stick they pushed purchases from the vendors' into the street and there picked them up. They spoke to no one without first moving downwind. Speaking above a whisper to anyone was forbidden. They never entered narrow walks where they might encounter others. They ate, drank, and slept only with others sharing their afflictions. Taverns and food shops were barred to them; wine and food were brought to them outdoors. They ate and drank only from their own bowls which they kept with them at all times and also used for begging, the only livelihood left them.

Europe received its second massive dose of this unholy disease from men who had gone forth to wage holy war. Leprosy appeared in northern Europe during the sixth and seventh centuries, with the return of Christian crusaders from the Middle East, and spread radpily.

The spread proved to be a blessing in disguise. Out of it came further isolation, tortures, and death, true. There came also something else: hospitals.

Leprosaria, or leprosy institutions, were nothing new. Gregory of Tours (538?-593), the Frankish cleric and historian, mentions one. As leprosy spread during the 11th, 12th and 13th centuries, the advantage of such retreats as isolation pockets became apparent. There were just too many leprous people about to exile them all to the wilderness pest huts; the wilderness was filling up.

Europe's first known leprosarium since the one mentioned by Gregory of Tours was the work of Ruy Diaz de Bivar in 1067 in Spain. Diaz de Bivar (1040?-1099) is better known by a more monumental name: El Cid, national hero of Spain.

The concept of the lazar house or lazaretto, as leprosaria were called, appealed to the French. Within decades there were more than 2,000 in France. The English opened more than 200.

By the 13th century there were more than 19,000 lazarettos in Europe. The name springs from the Italian word for leper, *lazzaro*, after a passage in St. Luke in the Bible describing how a rich man ignored ". . . a certain beggar named Lazarus, which was laid at his gate, full of sores."

To view the lazar house as a token of enlightenment is to misjudge the times, however. There were few comforts there. Isolation was its only purpose, neglect its only medicine, death generally its only exit. The lazar house's one advantage to inmates was, it stood as some shield against the abuses of the outside.

Banquet for lepers. Occasionally lepers were treated kindly. A banquet (as shown lower left) was a common gesture. A priest is shown hearing a leper's confession (center), masking his own face as he does so. The classic leper's rattle, shown at the kneeling man's belt, appears in all scenes.

German print, 1493.

Many chose to risk the outside nonetheless; the outside continued to be cruel.

Miraculous cures attributed to the holy relics of St. Walburga housed in the church at Eichstadt Germany, were denied the leprous except when priests chose to display them outdoors.

Late in the 12th century, the Catholic church decreed leprosy victims dead. Priests literally dragged them to cemeteries by the hand, forced them to kneel among gravestones, sprinkled earth on them and said, "Be thou dead to the world, but alive again with God."

Not everyone was so eager to assist the church and state sanctioned punishment of the unfortunate. In England, Gilbertus Anglicus, or Gilbert the Englishman (?-1250) studied the disease as a clinical rather than divine affliction. His account of leprosy is one of the few objective medieval accounts of the disease and for those who shared his objectivity, one of the few good sources of practical information. In the 13th century Hungarian Princess Elizabeth left a soft, comfortable court life to feed and bathe leprosy sufferers and died doing it age 24. Today she is known as St. Elizabeth, patron saint of those with leprosy.

The enlightened and kind were a minority.

England abolished the graveyard death rites and banishment and simply burned the leprous at the stake or piled like wood on bonfires.

The French clergy continued to read the funeral service but added a realistic touch. When it was over they buried their subjects alive or cemented them inside the walls of their refuges.

* * *

No accurate totals of leprosy cases and/or deaths have ever been available but almost surely the disease shoveled millions into their graves.

The disease achieved pandemic velocity in the 13th and 14th centuries. It peaked in the 15th. Then, it declined and quit. By mid-16th century, but for a few pockets here and there, leprosy was as much a part of the past as dinosaurs.

What was happening? Was this a Divine miracle?

Reasons are offered for leprosy's abrupt exit; none so far explain it fully. They include improved sanitary conditions, the numbers in which leprosy victims were killed off by their persecutors, loss of pathogenicity of *Mycobacterium leprae*, and the coincidental flash floods of plague that broke over Europe for 200 years from mid-14th to mid-16th centuries.

The last seems most plausible. Twenty-five million, or one quarter of Europe's people is a conservative estimate of deaths.

Those favoring the plague theory feel large numbers of leprotics were packed into gloomy hospitals, a concentration of physically drained people with one disease already, easily wiped out by the plague.

Survivors were too few and too scattered to ever spawn a new epidemic.

This too is unproven theory, however. To this day no one knows why leprosy retreated from Europe; another epidemiological puzzle still unsolved.

As leprosy diminished so did need for lazar houses. Two famous English leprosaria—the Hospital of St. Mary of Bethlehem, and Bridewell—were put to other humanitarian uses. St. Mary's became the mental institution called Bedlam in 1547. Bridewell was converted in 1553 to a prison for women where a crack on the jaw was thought a good way to start the day.

The lazar houses in France were closed in 1656. The Sun King Louis XIV (1638-1715) channeled the money from their sale into hospital construction.

Leprosy was not dead, of course, only traveling.

Explorers prowling the New World brought it everywhere. The major portion of western leprosy came with slaves from the endemic regions of Africa and it showed partiality to the tropics. North America, except for muggy regions in the South and West, attracted almost none. Central and South America, particularly Brazil, were sorely infected.

"The Lord giveth and the Lord taketh away," medieval clergy said by way of explaining the disappearance. If God had indeed laid the burden of leprosy on man it now appeared he was removing it, from Europe at least, and laying it on man elsewhere.

＊　　＊　　＊

Leprosy still persists, not embroiling entire continents, but it persists.

There are now 11,000,000 cases of leprosy in the world (WHO estimate), 2.8 million of them registered, meaning, under treatment. "Leprosy has had an almost worldwide distribution although it is now largely restricted to the tropics and subtropics," states a 1966 issue of the WHO *Bulletin*. Brazil currently lists 400 cases per 100,000 people in some areas, French Guiana 223 cases per 100,000.

"There have been recorded 'epidemic' periods in a number of clearly defined areas," the WHO *Bulletin* reports. "These include the Hawaiian Islands in the 19th century and on Nauru Island since 1912."

The U.S. has fewer than 3,000 cases of Hansen's Disease. About 300 of these are under treatment at the U.S. Public Health Service Hospital at Carville, Louisiana, the only such hospital in the continental United States. Hansen's Disease is leprosy's preferred name. It carries less stigma and excites less fear than does the word leprosy. Hansenite, or Hansenotic, are preferred in describing sufferers rather than "leper" for the same reasons.

Hansen's Disease is considered a communicable disease of the tropics primarily, and correctly so. In parts of Africa ten in every 100 are infected. The disease does appear in temperate zone countries, however (Crete, Japan, Korea), and in subarctic zone countries (Norway, Iceland). Only Canada and Siberia appear totally free.

There have been many supposed cure substances; quack and snake oil are their labels. For centuries there was only one known of any worth: Chaulmoogra oil, and more recently, its purified esters. Chaulmoogra is also used in treating arthritis and skin disorders. The drug can be applied locally, orally, and intravenously. Orientals have used it for 1,000 years. Chaulmoogra is ugly to taste and of limited and questionable value. It comes from the seeds of the *kalow*, a southeast Asian tree.

According to legend its discoverer was a prince who, infected with leprosy, exiled himself to the jungle to live out his remaining days. Hungry, he ate *kalow* seeds which cured his leprosy and that of a beautiful princess he met there and later married.

Modern therapy calls for sulfones, which are complex organic compounds. Sulfone therapy was first tried in 1940 on Hansen's victims at the Carville national leprosy center. After six months 25 per cent of the patients had improved; after three years, close to 100 per cent. The value of sulfone therapy is proven. Diamino-diphenyl-sulfone (DDS) and its derivatives promin and diasone are in wide use. But sulfone therapy is discouraging; two to five years are necessary to bring about arrest and retreat of the disease manifestations. The disease sometimes recurs during the course of treatment. Sulfones sometimes cause toxic side reactions.

In the late 1950's, a new drug called Ciba-1906, a diphenyl-thiourea compound, appeared in preliminary studies to be as effective as sulfones but less toxic.

A future hope, to choose just one, is for a breakthrough to immunization. As yet there is none. There seems to be a relationship worth exploring between natural leprosy immunization and the tuberculosis vaccine BCG. The letters BCG stands for Bacillus Calmette-Guerin, after Leon Calmette (1863-1933), and Camille Guerin (1872-1961), French bacteriologists who first immunized children against TB in 1924. Since 1939 in Argentina, leprologists have noticed that youngsters innoculated with BCG rarely contract Hansen's disease.

*   *   *

As the disease persists, so persists the fear and loathing of antiquity. Civilization and technology have never bred out leprohobia. Examples:

● Only 20 years ago "handling of lepers" qualified U.S. servicemen for extra hazardous duty pay.

● Current laws in South America bar Hansen's victims from any trade or calling requiring direct or indirect contact with healthy persons. There is no job anywhere outside a leprosarium which does not involve human contact.

● Doctors have gone on record refusing to treat leprosy patients for fear their other patients will desert them.

● All mail leaving the national leprosarium at Carville is sterilized, "only as a gesture of respect to the unconvinced and not because there is any scientific necessity for it," states each issue of the Carville *Star*.

● In some African countries leprosy is so feared that public health teams dare not say they are looking for it, else entire villages may turn hostile or simply hide. Instead they pretend they are examining patients for other skin diseases.

● In Korea a new clinic building was destroyed by villagers when they learned leprosy cases were to be treated with others.

● In China in June 1952 officials in a rural province ordered some 100 leprosy patients taken from a local hospital and burned alive.

The prejudice which persists is not found to comparable degree with any other disease.

The best that can be said for this prejudice is, abuses in its name today are generally not as monstrous as the recent medieval cremation in China. This is faint praise and small progress. The abuses now simply take subtler shapes, affecting research for example instead of the sufferer himself directly. Everything slow and inadequate about leprosy technology and administration can be blamed in some degree on this loathing and/or prejudice. Either one frightens away nations with money and people with brains.

There is indeed much that is slow, inadequate, and frustrating about leprology:

● Doctors retreat from its service (only three available for 500,000 patients in northern Nigeria in fall 1967). "Some of them are reluctant to be trained in leprosy for fear of having to remain for a long time in the work," a WHO report stated. ". . . Most of the doctors have a feeling that leprosy work is a service of some lower standard, some considering it even as a disciplinary measure . . . and the doctor is too often looked down on as a 'leprosy doctor,' sometimes with repercussions on his family and social life."

● No wonder drug exists. Penicillin cures yaws,for example, in one day. The best leprosy drug is still DDS. Its treatment sometimes requires five years.

● There is little hope for a such a wonder drug as of now. Drug companies generally bear the burden of drug research. They are not interested in working up a fast leprosy cure. There is little profit in serving so comparatively few customers (12,000,000 in current drug economics is few), most of whom cannot afford treatment anyway. DDS costs one dollar per patient per year.

● There is still no true leprosy immunization in sight. BCG vaccination studies (Uganda in 1960, to name one) shows BCG confers substantial protection against early leprosy for about wo years, but this finding represents a research guidepost, not a final goal. There can be no vaccine until (1) *Mycobacterium leprae* can be cultivated *in vitro* on artificial media, and (2) experimental animals can be infected for study. These are the two major impediments in leprosy research.

Only with the first problem has effort achieved any success. Small colonies have been grown in mouse feet via innoculation with *Mycobacterium leprae*. This accomplishment is thus far of narrow research value. As for the second, there are still no experimental animals known which react to leprosy infection as humans do. Until some are found, study is hampered.

* * *

René Laennec (1781-1826), the brilliant French diagnostician who numbered invention of the stethoscope among his accomplishments, said: "Men need the truth dinned into their ears many times and from all sides. The first rumor makes them prick up their ears, the second registers, the third enters."

Thus it is with leprosy, in many ways a paper pestilence.

Though a communicable disease it is not easily communicable. In most circumstances it is actually less contagious than other communicable diseases; the bacillus is slothful in its growth. To contract the kind known as lepromatous leprosy one must have constant, close contact over years with a carrier. Neural leprosy seems all but impossible to contract; few cases of communicability are known.

If contracted the disease does not inevitably crumble limbs and disintegrate faces. It sometimes manifests itself as scaly skin and nothing more. Its ultimate end is not necessarily death. No one knows exactly why as yet, but leprosy patients sometimes recover without treatment. Those who contract leprosy can now be clinically cured. "Leprosy is only a disease," a WHO official once said, "not a disgrace."

Though repeated 10,000 times three, these truths still take a long time entering.

In the Rio Muni district of Spanish Guinea in 1940 a man was being whipped in the street by his village headman.

"What has he done?" a public health worker asked.

"Nothing," the headman grunted.

"Then what is the reason for whipping him?"

"He is a leper," the headman said, swinging his whip again. "Isn't that reason enough?"

PROFILE OF LEPROSY:

Definition: A chronic, endemic, bacterial, deforming affliction bearing strong resemblance to other diseases such as tuberculosis at times, and carrying agonizing social stigma. Also known as Hansen's Disease. Leprosy takes two major forms:

1—Type "L" or lepromatous; the infection lodges under the skin.

2—Type "N" or neural, affecting the nervous system. Both types may infect a single person simultaneously (called mixed L-N type) but their manifestations are distinctly different.

Symptoms: Gradual onset manifested by headaches, chills, mental depression. Numbness occurs in portions of the body where classic, severe symptoms will finally appear.

L type is by far the more destructive of the two. L type shows itself by discolored skin blotches (macules) sometimes ten inches across, erupting pimples (papules), and fleshy lumps (nodules). Hands and face appear swollen and bumpy. The face sometimes assumes a leonine appearance. Mucous membranes of upper respiratory tract are usually assaulted; the larynx degenerates, resulting in marked changes in voice quality. Blindness sometimes occurs. L type victims live 15 years after onset, average, before complications bring death.

N type is symptomized by whitening of the skin; persons exhibiting this type are sometimes described as "silver men." Peripheral nerves deaden, the resulting anesthesia leaving large skin areas without feeling or sensitivity to pain. There is muscle weakness and paralysis and sometimes a "claw hand" deformity. Extreme N type cases display atrophying skin, bone necrosis, and autoamputation of finger and toe joints. This is the so called "rotting" so widely feared. N type causes more deformity than L, and is sometimes totally crippling. Generally, however, it inflicts only mild or partial disability and is seldom fatal.

Fatality: Leprosy itself is rarely fatal; death is invariably due to complications.

Complications: Tuberculosis, enteric infections, and nephrosis are major killers, overwhelming long term patients in weak condition.

Infectious agent: Mycobacterium leprae. It cannot as yet be cultured. It will naturally but reluctantly multiply on mouse feet.

Occurrence: Five cases per 1,000 population in tropics. Equatorial Africa lists highest case rate; 10 per cent in some districts. One case per 1,000 in temperature climates. In Europe, Greece, Portugal, and Spain show low endemicity. It is endemic but decreasing in Hawaii, at low level in the Canal Zone, Puerto Rico, and the Virgin Islands. Chief U.S. focus is southeast Texas; 20 or so cases yearly. Occasional cases appear in Louisiana, Florida, and California. It is almost nonexistent but nonetheless present in Norway and Iceland. World total: 12,-000,000 current infections, half of those in China, Korea, and Japan.

Reservoir: Man.

Infection source: Discharges from lesions of infected persons.

Transmission: Routes and methods uncertain.

Portal of infection: Also uncertain. The bacillus possibly enters through skin or mucous membranes of upper respiratory tract.

Incubation: Seven months to 30 years. *Average:* three to five years.

Communicability period: Conceivably endless. Disease is definitely communicable as long as lesions discharge bacilli. Patients who demonstrate bacilli are considered infectious even when lesions are not present.

Susceptibility: Universal. Most likely victims are infants. Resistance increases with age. Adults remain susceptible if never exposed as children. Natural reactivity to the leprosy test substance lepromin (prepared from lepromatous nodules of patients) indicates possibility of resistance to some degree. Reactivity is absent in L type cases, L type being more malignant. N type patients frequently show reactivity. Healthy persons do also. BCG brings on positive lepromin reaction in about 97 per cent of persons. Lepromin is therefore of little diagnostic use.

Specific treatment: Sulfone drugs, preferably diamino-diphenyl-sulfone (DDS) and its derivatives promin and diasone. Drugs are taken orally. Small initial doses are slowly increased to match a patient's maximum tolerance. Drug therapy lasts two to five years. In event sulfones fail or sicken the patient, thiourea derivatives, long acting sulfonamides or thiosemicarbazone are recommended.

Prevention:

1—Separate children from leprous parents.

2—Teach population methods of transmission. Explain risk is greater at early ages, hopefully so leprous adults will cooperate in remaining apart from their children.

3—Send out mobile field teams for survey and treatment in known leprosy areas; also, play down fearful aspects.

Control:

1—Report all cases. Reports are obligatory in most states of U.S.

2—Compulsory and indiscriminate segregation is often employed until patient is bacteriologically negative for six months or more. These measures are not necessary or wise. Isolation of individuals blocks leprosy campaigns directed to masses. Mass attendance at clinics is more desirable. In areas where leprosy is rare, home isolation suffices, but avoid patient contact with children.

3—Disinfect patients' lesions and articles.

4—Quarantine and/or BCG immunization: value not yet proved.

5—Ferret out patient contact for testing and treatment. This is generally difficult. Too much time passes between exposure and recognition of disease. A patient may contact many persons for years before he knows he himself has the disease.

Basic public health measures during epidemics: Same as above but on larger scale: mass bacteriological diagnosis, treatment, investigation, separation of children from leprous parents.

International measures: None. Containment policies and travel regulations are vague and discretionary.

"Le Malade." Daumier portrayed malaria as a slow, languid way of dying. Malaria was widespread in 19th century France.

World Health Organization.

V MALARIA

"Malaria history is a sequence of needs and discoveries stimulated by war."

Malaria has many names.

Its original is Italian, *mala aria,* meaning literally "bad air." For centuries its cause was imagined to be the overwhelming stinks of the swamps. A Greek word for it is *elonosia,* a French one, *paludisme,* and an English language one, miasma, all meaning swamp fever. Britons called it marsh poison, the white man's grave, and ague, the last still used to describe any alternating fever-and-chill attack. Ague comes from the Latin *acuta,* meaning sharp.

Voltaire was so agitated upon learning ague has two syllables while plague has but one that he cried: "May plague take one half of the English dictionary and ague the other!"

Malaria is the name in current employ in most languages, though its meaning is archaic rather than accurate. Malaria's true cause, a protozoan parasite of the genus *Plasmodium,* not bad air, is known everywhere.

Few pestilences have brutalized mankind in more criminal fashion than malaria. Every nation afflicted has suffered change for the worse in fortune: malaria is thought to be one of the forces which toppled Rome.

Armies have been defeated and routed by malaria. The disease measures up in deadliness to the yardstick for all pestilence, the plague. Malaria epidemics have enveloped millions and buried one in every ten victims. In company with another mosquito borne disease, yellow fever, malaria almost halted for good the construction of the Panama Canal.

In some African localities it still results in death for one victim in ten, particularly children below age three (WHO estimate).

After death, malaria's second monstrous result (considered its primary one by some epidemiologists) is the chronic invalidism that saps populations. Malaria, lacking the spectacular symptoms of cholera and leprosy, is insidious rather than dramatic in effect, except when it bursts into epidemic. It quietly assists other diseases in causing great numbers of deaths. It stifles physical and mental growth and depresses fertility and birth rates. It bars development of potentially fertile areas by its presence. It forces abandonment of already productive areas by its arrival. By its attrition of human beings, malaria lames more agriculture and industry, stifles more ambition and reverses more progress than any other communicable disease.

Modern malariologists can alter these depressing circumstances; malaria technology and problems are well understood. Still, it is the most ubiquitous of communicable diseases. Though principally a tropical disease it has appeared as far north as Archangel, USSR (64° north latitude) and as far south as Cordoba in Argentina 32° south latitude). There are still 100,000,000 new cases yearly.

*   *   *

Diseases have plagued higher life forms since their beginnings. Fossils reveal osteomyelitis and tooth cavities pained reptiles 21,000,000 years ago.

Malaria is an old timer, almost certainly older than man. Mosquitoes have been found preserved in resin lumps formed during the reptilian age. Vulnerability of anthropoid apes to certain malarias offers strong possibility that their ancestors suffered malaria before man appeared.

Malaria probably first appeared in Africa, believed to be the birthplace of the human species. From there its creepers reached toward the Mediterranean, to India, to southeast Asia. Malaria's journey to the western hemisphere still wants mapping; its course has never been traced. It was possibly already endemic in Latin America when the first explorers arrived from Europe. Settlers in North America called it Indian ague.

There is no doubt that malaria plagued ancient civilizations.

Homer's tenth *Iliad* describes an epidemic attacking "mules, swift dogs, and men," imagined to be afflicted by arrows of the god Apollo. The armies battling at Troy may have been the first ever touched by malaria.

During the second millenium B.C. Asiatic Indians described an attack in which "the belly, with enlarged spleen that distends the left side, is hard as stone and arched like the back of a turtle." It appeared most frequently in autumn and was characterized by fevers and chills every second or third day. Indians called it the "King of Diseases," and in this case its identity is not in doubt. Enlarged spleen, seasonal occurence, intermittent fever and chills are all malaria symptoms.

Old Egyptian temple hieroglyphics yield the expression "Aat," meaning malarious or a disease surely malaria. To careful people, anywhere it was "Aat" was a swampy, unhealthy place.

In ancient China a disease undoubtedly malaria was believed to be an onslaught by three allied demons. The first demon beat the victim about the head with a hammer to produce headaches. The second doused him with pails of freezing water to make him shiver. The third demon roasted him with torches to cause fever.

The old Greeks also realized that certain diseases peaked on definite predictable days. One which did so again and again and again was a feverish sickness probably malaria. Few diseases ebb and flow in more regular cycles.

They also correctly sensed a link between disease and seasonal weather changes, particularly between malarial fevers and rainy weather, though for wrong reasons. They imagined the dampness to be fouling the atmosphere and creating *elonosia*. It was actually lending comfort to vector mosquitoes in their breeding.

While everyone among the Greeks talked about the weather and swamps, finally one of the philosopher-physicians did something about it. The motivation ascribed to Empedocles of Agrigentum in Sicily (504-433 B.C.) is perhaps born of imaginative legend but his accomplishment is real.

Empedocles supposedly gagged on a particularly heavy dose of *elonosia* while at Silenus, a city then reeling with seasonal malaria. He reasoned, if swamp air is so offensive and pestilential, why not get rid of it by cleaning the swamp? With work crews building dams and digging drainage ditches, he diverted two sweet water streams into the marshes to flush them. It is said the malaria epidemic ended shortly afterward.

Empedocles was possibly the first malaria sanitarian, surely the first of any reputation. He established the principle still basic in malaria control, namely, drain wet areas. The Sicilians struck coins and raised columns in his honorable name.

Outside Sicily the accomplishment received mixed notices.

The Romans noted it carefully and made marsh draining mandatory in their exacting public health programs.

Others forgot it in time and its lesson was forgotten with it. The moats of the walled medieval cities bred mosquito swarms and filled the air with smells.

The Hippocratic *Epidemics* accurately describe the disease-swamp-weather relationship and the enlarged spleen symptom known to the Indians. For all its obvious prevalence, however, there is little mention of malaria plaguing the far ranging fourth century B.C. Greek armies of Philip II of Macedon (382-336 B.C.) and his son and heir Alexander. It can be assumed they *were* hurt in malarious lands and Alexander for one should have paid it more heed. Malaria complicated by alcoholism killed him in Babylon.

The Greeks also knew of a five-leaved plant, name now uncertain, which seemed to soften the effects of malarial attack. It is recommended in Hippocratic journals. Pedanius Dioscorides, a first century Greek botonist and army surgeon who served Roman Emperor Nero Claudius Caesar (37-68), refined the Hippocratic prescription. Three leaves, he said, should be taken by those wracked by fever every third day and four leaves by those whose fever came in four-day cycles. Dioscorides' real contribution to medicine and epidemiology was his organization of a disorderly medical botany into an applied science.

No one can say for certain who was the first man to conceive of mosquito netting, but again legend fills a blank that fact cannot. He may well have been the aggravated Phoenician who supposedly pulled his bedroom curtains down about himself one night while swatting at insects, and, wrapped in folds of gauzy material noticed several mosquitoes clinging outside, unable to touch his skin.

The Roman poets Horace (65-8 B.C.) and Juvenal (60?-140) both refer to netting (*conopeum*) especially designed to keep mosquitoes from sleeping men.

Over time, the role insects play in malaria transmission occurred to individuals now and again but only vaguely so. One was a first century Roman soldier and farmer concerned with selecting sites for country estates. Lucius Columella wrote:

> There should be no marshlands near the buildings
> . . . for [they] throw off a baneful stench in hot
> weather and breed insects armed with annoying stings
> . . . from which are often contracted mysterious dis-
> eases whose causes are even beyond the understanding
> of physicians. . . .

During subsequent centuries, there was always malaria. It did not incinerate entire populations as did plague. Nor did it bring torture and exile to its individual victims as leprosy did; mere chills and fevers do not excite such horror as a rotting, leprous face does. Yet, in Europe, Africa, Asia, in the New World, north latitudes and south, like the very bad air blamed for carrying it, it was always there, infecting millions.

※　　※　　※

During the Middle Ages malaria appears in references to unholy things as often as the devil does. Netting, drainage, the obvious mosquito-disease connection were neglected.

Malaria was likely the undoing of Mesopotamia. More than 30,000,000 lived there during the reign of Harun al Rashid (764?-809), the inquisitive sultan who often moved among his people in disguise to plumb public sentiment. They raised grain and fruit for the world on the black soil between the Tigris and Euphrates Rivers. After al Rashid's time, an intermittent fever disease, most likely malaria, moved across the land. Those not sickened and buried by it fled from it to healthier places. There were not enough people to till the land; it is axiomatic that untilled land becomes waste land. Thus it was with Mesopotamia and it has never quite recovered. About 5,000,000 live there today.

During the First Crusade, in 1098, some 300,000 men and 7,000 horses were thrown against Antioch. A year later in 1099, only 60,000 men still lived, and so few horses walked they were hardly worth counting. Epidemics took more of these than did Saracen swords and arrows. Malaria was almost certainly one of them.

Some authorities dispute existence of the intermittent fevers in pre-Columbian America. If they are correct, if there were none, they certainly came in on the ships of the early *conquistadores*, and with the first slaves brought from Africa to the West Indies in 1501.

Spider amulets appear on the list of standard colonial American cures for the disease they called Indian ague. The spider was worn live, around the neck, in a nutshell.

African and American Negroes nailed or tied locks of malaria victims' hair to a tree to pass the fevers and chills to the tree itself.

Europeans traveling to steamy colonies relied upon nostrums reputed to be capable of repelling malaria and anything else one could name, including cancer. Daffy's Elixir, Singleton's Golden Eye Ointment, and Dr. Immanuel's Pills were three.

Their value is aptly described by a saying of the period: "Nature cures the diseases while the remedy amuses the patient." None truly performed as promised.

Certainly none helped Donna Francisca Henriques de Ribera (1576-1639), wife of the Count of Chinchon, then Viceroy of Peru. When the intermittent fevers bedded her in Lima in 1620, she sought relief in powdered bark from a local "fever tree" brought by an Indian. The man said his people had used the bark for so long that memory could not span the time.

The fever bark did more than just relieve chills and fever. To the delight of countess, husband, and doctor, it appeared to have driven the disease from her body and cured her.

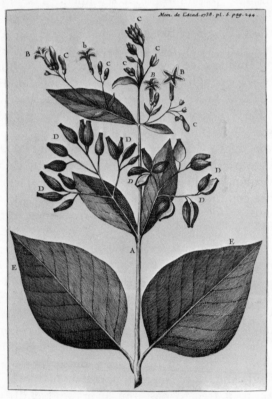

*An 18th century engraving. Details of
cinchona leaves and bark.*
World Health Organization

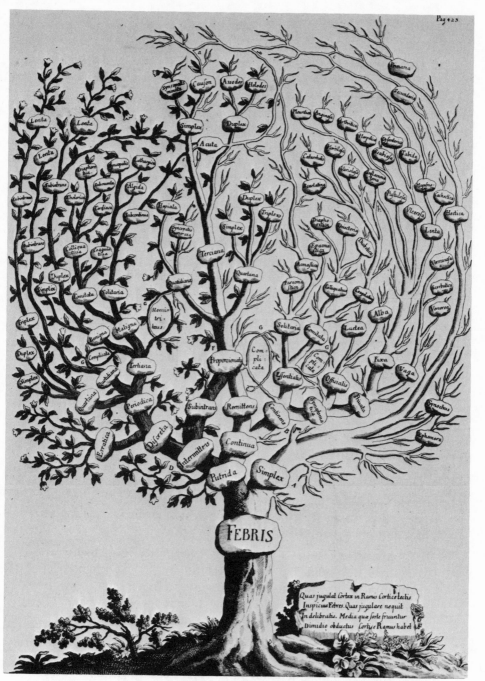

The Fever Tree. An engraving from an old pharmacopoeia. Fevers cured by cinchona are named on the branches having bark (the dark ones). Those not responding to cinchona are listed on those without bark (light). Illnesses sometimes cured are named on the half-stripped branches.

World Health Organization

This popular account may not be accurate; one historian disputes another on it. But this much is known: The tree (now called cinchona) came to the attention of European physicians in Peru in 1630. It possessed swift positive healing power never before seen in drugs. It was the first cure ever for the intermittent fevers.

The healing power of cinchona bark was the substance called quinine today. And after its dramatic cure of the Countess of Chinchon in Peru in 1630, medical practice the world over was never the same again. By its astounding ability to rapidly cure protracted fevers, it slowly took hold and ended forever a theory prevailing for 20 centuries, namely, that disease was caused by "corruption of humors." Only by "voiding corrupt humors" could disease be cured. The voiding sometimes required months. (From ancient times in both India and Greece the body was thought to be composed of various juices, or humors. The Greeks believed in four: blood, phlegm, black bile, yellow bile.) In destroying the humors-oriented practice, cinchona bark did not leave a vacuum. It opened the way to another practice: modern chemotherapy.

Bernardo Ramazzini (1633-1714), an Italian epidemiologist, said cinchona bark did for medicine what gunpowder had done for war.

꙳   ꙳   ꙳

Oliver Wendell Holmes (1809-1894), father of the U.S. Supreme Court justice of the same name, was an anatomy professor and author of essays and medical texts more lucid than most. He once wrote:

> Medicine . . . appropriates everything from every
> source that can be of slightest use . . . . It learned
> from a monk how to use antimony, from a Jesuit how
> to cure ague, from a friar how to cut for stone, from
> a soldier how to treat gout, from a sailor how to
> sound the eustachian tube. . . .

The Jesuit who cured ague was the Jesuit (or several Jesuits) priest who brought cinchona bark from Peru to Europe. There it was soon called Jesuit's bark by churchmen championing its use. The Jesuit endorsement was one of the big advertising blunders of history.

It was soon called other things less grand; Protestant factions which would damn anything Catholic damned the bark as a Vatican fraud.

This was a time when malaria was one of several epidemic diseases wasting Europe in turns or together. In high places, at least, feelings on Jesuits' or cinchona bark polarized around religious issues.

In England the Protestant Oliver Cromwell (1599-1658), fell ill with malaria. Supposedly because either Cromwell, his physicians, or both refused to use the "Popish powder," the Lord Protector of England died.

In France, King Louis XIV, a Catholic, also contracted the disease. He readily used the Jesuits' bark and lived.

For every cure there was complaint about the Jesuit's bark and with good reason. Dosage was difficult to determine. Patients were either made ill by overdose or left uncured by underdose. Quacks peddled inferior bark, or sometimes just any bark. "Fever Tree Frauds" ground up ordinary cinhcona, called it a secret remedy by some other name, and sold it to persons afraid to use cinchona at many times its going price.

There were failures and successes with cinchona bark and its quinine compound, which was finally extracted in 1820 by two French chemists.

In India in 1804 an English naval surgeon lost the first patient he ever treated with cinchona. Thirty-five years passed before anyone in India prescribed cinchona preparations for malaria.

Cinchona bark and its quinine derivatives were the only barriers in Africa between missionaries, explorers, and traders and a malaria grave. Object lessons abounded. In 1805, malaria killed 40 of 45 men seeking the mouth of the Niger River. This expedition carried no bark. In 1854 a group supplied with quinine explored the same river and did not lose a man to malaria.

A common event in the history of disease is discovery of cure before cause is known. So it was with malaria. Quinine came first.

Then, 250 years later in 1880, French army doctor Charles Laveran (1845-1922), observed some pigmented bodies in the red blood of malaria patients in Algeria and filled the second blank.

The colored spots were plasmodia, the protozoan parasites which cause the disease.

A third major question was answered next, that concerning transmission. Research workers had proven filariasis to be a mosquito-borne disease. Donald Ross (1857-1932) of the Indian Medical Service speculated on mosquitoes carrying malaria, the thought offered and ignored several times earlier in history. Ross' intuition proved correct. *Anopheles* was indeed the vector. By incredibly difficult micro-dissections in 1897 Ross determined the malaria parasite completes its life cycle in the *Anopheles* mosquito's salivary gland. It is squirted from this gland to infect man when next the mosquito bites.

He wrote a poem to his wife to celebrate the discovery.

Ross received the Nobel Prize in 1902. The name *Anopheles* is Greek. It means "harmful and useless."

With the vector identified, formula for its destruction was a matter for chemists and devised easily. Swamp drainage was supplemented with larvicides (Paris green) floated onto swamps, puddles, any still water where mosquitoes deposited eggs and the larvae bred. The sanitarians became skilled at their new profession, tracing breeding grounds to the most obscure places. There is the classic story of an area being reinfected by mosquitoes breeding under a house in a single rain-filled soup can.

Effectiveness of linked drainage-larvicide control was demonstrated in Cuba and in the Panama Canal Zone from 1899 to 1944. There is probably not a marshier, buggier place in the world than the Isthmus of Panama. The canal could not have been built across it without mosquito control.

*　　*　　*

Dr. Gabriele Gramiccia of the WHO Malaria Intelligence Unit stated in fall of 1967: "The history of malaria is that of a sequence of needs and discoveries stimulated by war."

Malaria, once almost as much a part of Russia as its steppes, sickened 3,200,000 in 1914 in coincidence with the outbreak of hostilities. By 1922 malaria was blanketing the great land space, in consort with smallpox, cholera, typhus, and starvation. It broke out in unlikely areas, the Arctic Sea for one, at Archangel. In 1923 there were 6,000,000 cases registered, probably only a third of the true number. It was found that anopheline vector mosquitoes took shelter in the warm peasant huts in winter and infected many infants. Four in every ten died in areas short of quinine. Overall mortality was about 60,000 that year..

German armies striking at Greece in 1940 during World War Two found the partisan groups were not the only enemies. They also had to cope with malaria. In Russia, particularly in the Crimea, malaria was so threatening to offensive movement the German high command had to drain off manpower for control projects.

Others stimulated to malaria research on a grand scale by World War Two were the Allied Nations fighting the Japanese in the South Pacific. The reason was simple. The Japanese seized the Indonesian cinchona plantations, started in the 19th century from South American seeds, and yielding 20,000,000 tons of bark yearly. This was the largest single source and represented a true crop monopoly by the Dutch.

There were two efforts to create a new supply.

One, an American colonel carried a can of cinchona seeds and little more when evacuated as the Philippine Islands were falling to the Japanese in 1942. From these, new plantations were started in South America.

Two, some 14,000 other natural and synthetic compounds were screened. Atabrine was one. This substance was developed by German scientists, also motivated by wartime experience. British ships blockaded German troops at Salonika during World War One and cut off supplies, including quinine. Atabrine proved effective, and was used by U.S. forces in the South Pacific, but had one undesirable side effect. It colored the skin bright yellow.

Of the two efforts the synthetic program was the most productive; the wide spectrum of synthetic drugs available is part of its legacy. Some (proguanil and pyrimethamine) are preventatives. Others are fine for treatment (chloroquine, mentioned above, and amodiaquine). Still others (pamaquine)destroy parasite bodies loose in the blood, interrupting transmission from man to *Anopheles*. And some newer drugs (primaquine) guard the human body against malaria relapses.

Much current malaria chemotherapy has its roots in 1940's wartime research, as does insecticide technology.

Malaria control is one thing that did not suffer from the war. In fact, war has always stimulated medical discoveries. But malaria control did suffer from the war in the sense that land drainage, for example, was stopped for lack of manpower.

*   *   *

The larvicide-and-drainage control method has always had two flaws. It is costly to undertake and requires constant maintenance. Someone must frequently apply larvicide. Someone must almost constantly tend the draining. For treatment of limited areas larvicide and drainage are effective and practical. For large areas they are prohibitively expensive and sometimes impossible to sustain.

In 1935 South African research workers experimented with a new approach. They killed off adult mosquitoes with pyrethrum spray in dwellings and left the swamp larvae to breed as they pleased. This made sense. It is the adult, after all, which transmits malaria. The result of this pilot program was cheaper and easier malaria control. Reasons:

1—The moquito population was cut down.

2—Many died before the malaria parasites developed.

3—Many died before they could pass infection on to non-infected persons.

Still, to change over from larvae attack to adult mosquito attack required more tenacious substances than pyrethrum. Pyrethrum has a tendency to evaporate.

In 1938, dichloro-diphenyl-trichloro-ethane, an ordorless, crystalline, colorless, water insoluble organic compound first synthesized in 1872, was found to have extraordinary insecticidal properties. Sprayed on walls and ceiling it remained potent and deadly for months, a veritable ambush for any insect settling there. This had particular significance for malaria. *Anopheles* mosquitoes rest on walls after stinging, to digest their blood meals. It had a broad significance for mosquito control in general. The compound needed application only two or three times yearly in homes and other small areas. It needed no spreading over acres of mud or across a thousand water holes. Broad scope campaigns became more possible than ever. For easy identification dichloro-diphenyl-trichloro-ethane was called by its still current universal name, DDT.

There were those in public health who disapproved. To use DDT for control was to use only half its talents. They nagged instead about eradication, a concept often thought of but never thought of as possible, that is, ridding the earth of malaria forever. To paraphrase the Italian epidemiologist Ramazzini, what gunpowder did for war, DDT could do for malaria eradication. It made annihilation of a foe more possible than ever.

⁂ ⁂ ⁂

The delegates of the 14th Pan American Sanitary Conference in Santiago, Chile, in 1954, committed themselves to malaria eradication and recommended a global program. The Eighth World Health Assembly supported this vast notion in 1955. In 1957 WHO approved malaria eradication in principle and practice. The objective was the adult mosquito, not the larva.

The eradication program is still moving.

Malaria eradication does not mean extermination of the *Anopheles*; public health people are reluctant to create vacuums in nature, for reasons which are at present only intuitions. No one yet has determined the need or value of mosquitoes. They perform no service to anyone's knowledge. Yet, they evidently mean something to swallows. When a certain part of Greece was swept clean of mosquitoes in 1946, all the swallows left.

Eradication aims only to wipe out the parasite, to break the transmission cycle for three years, for falciparum and vivax malaria die out in infected individuals in this time. They are known as self-eradicating malarias. Therefore, the antimosquito measures stop, leaving the vector mosquitoes alive but without opportunity to become infected. There are no infected human reservoirs on which they can feed. This condition has a name: anophelism without malaria.

One country which has known anophelism without malaria for years, even before WHO eradication, is Switzerland. Malaria mosquitoes thrive there but there is no malaria. The last Swiss out break occurred at Basle during World War Two but was not home grown. It originated in war prisoner camps across the border in Germany.

Taiwan is one area which recently finished an eradication program with success. A WHO evaluation group certified Taiwan malaria free in November 1965.

Eradication is different from control and ultimately more complete:

1—Control attempts only reduction of disease incidence and is virtually a permanent committment of men and money.

2—Eradication eventually relieves the committment of men and money. By WHO definition, "Malaria eradication means the ending of the transmission of malaria and the elimination of the reservoir of infected cases in a campaign limited in time."

Any malaria eradication effort automatically seems to divide itself into four parts (see appendix):

1—Preparatory, or estimating the work to be covered, ordering equipment needed.

2—Attack. Total coverage spraying until it is proven transmission is interrupted and infection rates reduced to one person per 2,000 population or less.

3—Consolidation. Detection and mop-up of all missed, recurring and new cases.

The consolidation phase lasts at least three years. If no new cases appear at the end of that time, the eradication program passes into phase . . .

4—Maintenance. This means that routine public health services take over detection, reporting and treatment of new cases. Cases should be nonexistent.

Preventive and curative antimalarial drugs are used throughout the program.

Malaria eradication works.

Of the 148 countries which suffered from malaria, 47 now claim total eradication, some with, some without international organization assistance. For sheer size of effort, Soviet Russia is impressive. The Soviets began in 1962. Today all of the vast land space is malaria free. Spain, Taiwan, and Jamaica are three others. Sixty-eight countries now receive WHO assistance for malaria control or eradication.

What this means in numbers of people spared is most easily expressed as a proportion: In 1955 five sixths of all those living in the world's originally malarious areas were prey to malaria. In 1966 only one third were.

What this means to a nation's prosperity is best illustrated by subsequent growth. In Spain farmers have settled and are working once deserted land. Ceylonese rice production is up 50 per cent. Chimbote in Peru did not become an important coal and iron port until malaria eradication.

Not everyone agrees malaria eradication works well.

There is argument and confusion over the practicality of the current insecticide approach taken in the worldwide eradication program. In some countries, routine campaigns with residual insecticides have succeeded in bringing malaria incidence down to zero. In other countries, campaigns of identical quality have succeeded only in destroying mosquitoes; the malaria incidence remains the same.

Some in the very organizations working hardest on eradication believe too much is expected of it. One is Dr. K. Raska, chief of the WHO Communicable Diseases Division. He believes eradication is a reasonable goal to hope for but a difficult one. Beyond malaria, and also smallpox, he is pessimistic. "Eradication of all diseases is impossible, I feel," he said in fall 1967. "As old ones are killed off, new strains appear, or entirely new diseases. There will always be something."

Capricious programs which serve in one place but rebel in another are but one problem. The emergent country woods are full of them, malarial and nonmalarial in nature, particularly in Africa:

● *Anopheles* can suddenly display great resistance to residual insecticides. This talent for survival suddenly emerged in 1951 in Greece; mosquitoes landed on and flew from DDT sprayed walls when they should have been dropping dead.

● Suffering populations too have proven surprisingly resistant. In some parts of India people replaster their interior walls after every birth and death, and before each marriage. Each time a female menstruates, they plaster the floors. Walls are plastered ten times yearly, floors once a week. After each plastering the home must be resprayed with DDT. People object. Fear of criminal prosecution is a major reason for admitting the sprayers at all after each plastering.

● A black market in Cameroon once inflated the price of a five-centime antimalaria drug tablet to 50 centimes. The poor who needed the pill most could afford them least.

● Some governments have embarked on eradication without knowing whether they and their citizens could afford it, and found they couldn't. The same governments often are short of trained administrators and public health people. The result is setbacks. Such nations must also contend with distasteful, inequitable arithmetic. Eradication costs more in poor countries than in those better off.

In Italy and Greece per capita cost is one dollar per person per year, in Central Africa, four dollars. Any medical attention costing more than 1/100 of the average annual income costs too much. In Italy a dollar is only about 1/1500 of the annual figure. In Central Africa the four dollars is one tenth.

Lack of money, shortage of personnel are purely socio-economic problems. Socio-economic problems are the most grievous of all in international malaria eradication.

The Mexican government once calculated with some precision the cost of malaria sickness and death to the nation yearly in unearned income and unproduced goods. It was $156,000,000.

In 1959 WHO estimated the eradication bill for the entire globe will eventually total $1,691,000,000.

No one country will be heavily burdened. The money will come from many sources: The individual countries with malaria projects, WHO, International Children's Emergency Fund, UN Development Program, Pan American Health Organization, U.S. bilateral funds, the Columbo Plan of the British Commonwealth, and French FIDES funds, to name some which will cover the $1,691,000,000 cost.

By its own calculations the Mexican government alone is losing roughly that much every 11 years.

*   *   *

In the first 11 months of 1967 in South Vietnam, 7,540 American soldiers became victims of a new strain of falciparum parasite, the cause of malignant tertian malaria. (See Defnition, profile at chapter end.) Men stricken ran 104° F temperatures, and since they could barely stand, were withdrawn from combat and hospitalized. The new strain proved resistant to most drugs in the malaria pharmacopoeia, quinine and pyrimethamine excepted. It was first noticed in the mid-1960's and was considered so threatening to the war effort the U.S. allotted $11,-500,000 yearly to new drug research in some 150 laboratories.

Of 100,000 compounds tested, seven showed promise. From the seven, two likely candidates emerged.

One, oddly enough is the antileprosy drug diamino-diphenyl-sulfone, or DDS. It shows strong talent for both prevention and cure.

The second combines two antibacterial substances and destroys the parasite's ability to either live or reproduce in the human body.

In clinical trials 11 prisoner volunteers at Jackson County Jail in Kansas City, Missouri, were stung by *Anopheles* carrying the new strain or were injected with blood bearing it. Ten were reported cured by only one tablet. The 11th required two. Walter Reed Army Institute for Research in Washington said the antimalarial compound "looks good" and announced early field trials.

The history of malaria is indeed a sequence of needs and discoveries stimulated by war.

PROFILE OF MALARIA:

Definition: An acute, infectious, chronic, communicable disease occurring when protozoan parasites invade the red blood cells. The name is from the Italian *mala aria*, meaning "bad air." Foul smelling swamp air was once erroneously believed to be the cause.

Symptoms: Moderately swift onset, commonly beginning with overwhelming fatigue. Alternating tooth-rattling chill and rapidly escalating fevers to 104° F. Fever is accompanied by headache and vomiting; ends with flooding sweat. Fever, chills, sweating disappear for a time, then set in again, either daily, every third day or every fourth day, depending upon species of attacking parasite. This primary seizure (attack, rest, attack) continues for a week, perhaps a month, accompanied by spleen enlargement, anemia, jaundice.

There are four major malarias:

1—Benign tertian, or vivax, so called because severe paroxysms of chills and fever strike every third day.

2—Quartan. Attacks take place every fourth day. Fever-chill paroxysms are shorter, less severe, but parasites can remain in the blood for several years. It is relatively uncommon.

3—Malignant tertian (aestivo-autumnal), which is most severe symptomatically of all, but of shorter duration and without relapses. Malignant tertian often leads to death if not treated; it is a hot climate malaria.

4—Ovale, which is the rarest type, found only in coastal west Africa, shows only mild symptoms.

Fatality: Death claims as many as 10 per cent of the untreated cases. Among treated cases the toll is seldom higher than 0.5 per cent.

Complications: Concurrent infections taking advantage of a victim's weakened condition. Such infections often cause death.

Infectious agents:

1—For benign tertian malaria, *Plasmodium vivax.*

2—Causing quartan malaria, *Plasmodium malariae.*

3—Malignant tertian, *Plasmodium falciparum.*

4—Ovale malaria is caused by *Plasmodium ovale.*

Occurrence: Malaria is endemic to tropics and subtropics everywhere. Modern control measures have reduced or eliminated incidence in many areas. During the past 15 years control and eradication measures have slashed malaria case numbers from 250 million per year, with 2,500,000 deaths, to less than 100,000,000 cases (WHO estimates). Certain temperate zone countries have been endemic foci (Greece, Italy, for two); here too controls have done much to eliminate malaria.

Reservoir: Man is the only significant reservoir. Primates may harbor *Plasmodium malariae.*

Infection source: Female *Anopheles* mosquito.

Transmission: Via a complex man-vector-man cycle; the parasite undergoes certain sexual and developmental changes in each.

The mechanics of the process:

1—A female anopheline mosquito "bites" and sucks up human blood infected with sexual forms of malaria plasmodia (parasites). At this moment the mosquito becomes the definitive host.

2—Cysts produced by the sexual malaria parasites develop in the mosquito's stomach wall in eight to 35 days, depending upon plasmodia species and temperatures in which the mosquito lives.

3—Malaria parasites, fully developed and multiplied make their way to the mosquito's salivary gland. There they await injection into another man.

4—The next healthy person bitten by the mosquito vector becomes infected. At this moment of sting the person becomes the susceptible host.

5—The parasites develop in the liver of this newly infected susceptible host. This breeding phase coincides with attacks of malaria, with fever, anemia, and other symptoms often leading to death.

6—Sexual forms of the parasite appear in the red blood cells 14 days after onset of symptoms, ready to be picked up by another anopheline mosquito and carried to still other persons.

Malaria may also be transmitted in blood donations from infected persons. Drug addicts sometimes pass along malaria in sharing contaminated needles.

Portal of infection: Through skin by injection as described above.

Incubation: It varies with plasmodium species:

1—*Plasmodium vivax*, 14 days. With some strains, however, the primary attack may be delayed eight to ten months. This delay is known as protracted incubation.

2—*Plasmodium malariae*, 30 days.

3—*Plasmodium falciparum*, 12 days average.

4—*Plasmodium ovale*, 14 days.

In cases of blood transfusion infection, incubation is short.

Communicability period: Malaria is communicable as long as infective gametocytes remain in patient's blood. Times varies with parasite species and strain, and patient's response to therapy. Communicability runs from one to three years if infection is *Plasmodium vivax*, rarely more than one year if *Plasmodium falciparum*. Beyond these times, these species are no longer infective and are known as self-liquidating malarias. *Plasmodium malariae* infectivity may continue indefinitely but this too is generally self-liquidating after three years.

The mosquito, once infected, remains so for life; this lasts about a month.

Susceptibility: Everyone is susceptible. Previous infection, however, seems to grant some degree of immunity. Individuals may develop tolerance to effects in endemic areas where infection is continuous over years.

Resistance: Tolerance may develop upon repeated infection.

Specific treatment: Any one of several drugs, depending upon severity of attack, prior immunity, weight and age of patient. Some common drugs are: chloroquine diphosphate or sulfate, amodiquine dihydrochloride dihydrate, and mepacrine methane sulfonate. *Note:* Newly emerging falciparum strains in Vietnam and elsewhere prove resistant to all drugs but quinine.

Prevention:

1—Apply residual inscticide (DDT) or organophosphates (malathion) or carbamates (sevin) to homes, other places, where vector mosquitoes rest. Saturation over four consecutive years proves effective in regional eradication. *Note:* Residual spraying is the broadest, most effective, longest lasting preventive measure. Without it no eradication program is effective.

2—Spray homes nightly when residual insecticide is unavailable. Hang screens and bed nets. Douse skin with insect repellent.

3—Fill and/or drain vector mosquito breeding places, which usually are swamps, uncovered pools, et cetera.

4—Supply suppressive drugs (chloroquine diphosphate or sulfate, for one) to uninfected persons in malarious areas.

5—Treat chronic and acute cases. *Note:* This is vital to malaria control. Treatment of infected helps break the transmission chain.

Control of patients, contacts, environment:

1—Submit standard reports to public health agencies; usually required by regulation.

2—Isolation and/or quarantine is unnecessary. Infected patients are screened by nets.

3—Repeat residual spraying anywhere new or relapsing cases appear.

4—No artificial immunization is available. Therefore, determine previous infections among patient's contacts, locate reservoir if possible. *Note:* Location is important in advanced eradication program areas. Assume every feverish person has malaria and treat accordingly with drugs even before blood examination readings are in.

Basic public health measures during epidemics: First, survey the infected area to outline size of the epidemic. Follow with residual spray, suppressive drugs, treatment for infected, surveillance, sanitary measures mentioned above.

International measures: Disinsectize ships, planes, autos, trains on arrival from other countries if vector import is suspected. Disinsectize on departure.

Enforce rigid drain-and-fill measures within mosquito flying range of all sea and air ports to seal up breeding places.

When necessary, administer antimalarial drugs to individuals in mass movements (seasonal workers, for example) into any malaria-clean area.

VI BILHARZIASIS

the 25 year weariness

Two other remarkably dangerous but little known parasitic diseases (their inclusion by no means rounding out the parasitic family portrait) are bilharziasis and onchocerciasis.

Both are caused by worms visible to the naked eye, those of bilharziasis almost an inch long, those of onchocerciasis less than a millimeter. Both are tropical diseases. They are laying waste the lands where they are endemic and sabotaging the well being and ambition of the millions they infect.

Bilharziasis is so old it was known to the pharaonic Egyptians.

Onchocerciasis (the following chapter) is so new in a sense that it barely has a history at all.

*   *   *

Bilharziasis places number two to malaria among parasitic diseases as causes of suffering and precursor to death. It has an elastic epidemiological profile. It gives way in some areas (Israel and Japan) and swells in others (India and Libya) and the swelling far exceeds the shrinkage. More than 20 countries regard it as their major public health problem. More than 200,000,000 throughout the world are infected by schistosomes, or blood flukes, worms which cause this disease. Another name for bilharziasis is schistosomiasis.

Bilharziasis is griping to the guts, nauseating, corrosive to one's vitality, and often leads to death. Bilharziasis takes three clinical shapes, one which settles in the urinary bladder. The other two attack the small and large intestines. A major symptom of all three is crimsoning of the urine with blood.

Bilharziasis is a hot climate disease. It is one which few in the affluent temperate climate countries know, yet it is largely responsible for the colonialist inspired myth which states African Negroes are basically lazy. African populations were indeed slow moving because so many were drained of energy by bilharziasis and other tropic horrors.

97

Movement represents great effort. Bilharziasis tires a man to such degree he is close to death without knowing it. A sudden exertion can kill a bilharziasis sufferer. It used to be that native constabulary trainees, on their first day of vigorous training under European drill masters, dropped dead.

Like malaria, the major parasitic disease, bilharziasis' greatest penalty is the mass chronic invalidism it produces, which in turn retards progress and dries up ambition. In its *Third Report on the World Health Situation*, WHO's distressing assessment of the price the world pays for this disease reads in part:

In the majority of endemic areas, the infection is either static or is actually spreading. Recent surveys have established three facts. First there is an increased prevalence in some known endemic areas. Secondly, the infection has been spreading to immigrants in newly developed areas. Finally, the existence of foci not previously reported has been proved, for example, a small focus appears to be [bilharziasis] in India . . . in southern Thailand . . . in Lebanon and Libya. . . .

There is increasing evidence to suggest that bilharziasis is an important cause both of morbidity and mortality, particularly among younger people. Systematic studies of individuals and communities have established that severe and even fatal lesions of the urinary tract, liver, and lungs due to bilharziasis are very common in the United Arab Republic. It is known also that in parts of South America as many as 12 per cent of hospital autopsies show that death was a consequence of bilharzial infection. In the United Republic of Tanzania, about 20 per cent of its young people have already suffered what could prove to be serious and irreversible damage to the urinary tract. All these pathological changes are common in young children, but their effects become more serious in adolescent and early adult life.

. . . the public health importance and economic significance of bilharziasis have not hitherto been fully appreciated . . . bilharziasis control must be based on comprehensive epidemiological surveys of molluscs [fresh water snails are vectors] as well as of human beings and other vertebrate hosts and on improved irrigation and drainage coupled with the use of molluscicides

. . . . Nevertheless, control of the disease tended to be difficult and disappointing.

Bilharziasis' increased prevalence has direct link to new irrigation projects found in, and necessary to, so many emerging tropical nations. Dams create new lakes. Lands reclaimed for farms require irrigation ditches. Both are fine new breeding places for the vector snails. Economic development can be a mixed blessing.

Not one of bilharziasis' three varieties is indigenous to North America. A case appearing in the United States almost surely is imported. Doctors refer to bilharziasis as a "tourist disease." Soldiers returning from the South Pacific in World War Two were sometimes bearers; so were immigrants from South America. Today its victims are invariably travelers recently home from abroad. Cheaper and faster air travel promote the spread of this disease as it does cholera. More people travel to more places. Those infected with any disease (bilharziasis is just one) often arrive home before symptoms appear.

*   *   *

The three varieties of the disease, in their order of discovery, are: (1) Vesical or urinary bilharziasis, caused by a blood fluke or, more properly, a schistosome called *Schistosoma haematobium*. This worm grows to an inch in length sometimes and lives in the veins of man's urinary bladder. (2) Manson's bilharziasis, caused by *Schistosoma mansoni*, lodging in the large intestine. (3) Oriental or Asiatic bilharziasis. *Schistosoma japonicum* is the organism. It makes the small intestine walls its home.

Its transmission is completed by a complex man-water snail-man route. Man excretes eggs of the infective organism. These eggs enter streams, ponds, et cetera, either by direct defecation and urination or dumping. The eggs hatch. The liberated larvae find their way to a snail, enter, and a few weeks later are discharged again in another stage of development, much resembling wiggling tadpoles. The wigglers contact an animal host in the water, preferably man, they drill through the skin, enter the blood, incubate in the liver, and mature to full size worms or schistosomes. They finally take up residence in either bladder, large intestine, or small intestine, choice dictated by their kind. There the females pump out millions of eggs, sometimes for 20 years, which make their way into a man's urine and feces to commence the cycle again.

Not just an snail will do for the intermediate growth stage. Each stripe of bilharziasis has its preferred snail. The larvae can breed in no other. This limitation has played an important role in the way bilharziasis spreads, since not all three kinds of snails thrive everywhere.

※   ※   ※

Long before bilharziasis received its present name it was known as *aaa* (pronunciation uncertain) and probably first appeared in the Nile River Basin.

From the multitude of remedies for haematuria, or discharge of blood in urine, noted in pre-Christian payrus scrolls, it must be assumed the Egyptians and Mesopotamians knew of bilharziasis. The first known reference to the bloody urine condition appears in the Gynecological Papyrus of Kahun, dated at about 1900 B.C. This was found with another script pertaining to veterinary medicine at the ruined town of Kahun in 1893, hence the name. They are among the oldest medical papyri known.

The Ebers Papyrus, dated 1550 B.C. refers to a bloody urine condition, *aaa*, represented in hieroglyphic form by a penis and scrotum symbol. Twenty remedies are prescribed therein. One, "to kill worms in the body that have been caused by *aaa* disease" is: "Bake a cake in the shape of a phallus. Recite a certain magical formula over it. Wrap the cake in fatty meat. Give it to a cat."

The Ebers script was found by Georg Ebers (1837-1898) at Thebes in 1872. It consists of 110 columns totalling 2,289 lines of medical and remedial references. Supposition of vesical bilharziasis in old Egypt has since yielded to proof of it. In 1910 calcified *Schistosoma haematobium* eggs were found in two mummies of the 20th Dynasty, 1250 to 1000 B.C.

From the ancestral Nile Basin home it traveled, and as other diseases have done, it moved along routes followed by Arab pilgrims, merchants, and slave traders raiding the villages of central Africa for the humans which sold so profitably in Rome. On a map, bilharziasis' endemic areas and the Islamic cultural orbit coincide.

South African tribesmen have believed for centuries that their bloody urine condition was caused by something which entered the orifice of the penis while bathing. The Zulus wore basket-weave phallocrypts as defense.

Medieval Arab historians described "menstruating Egyptian males."

Bilharziasis came to the new world on the slave ships bringing "live cargo" from equatorial Africa in the 16th, 17th, and 18th centuries. It swept through the West Indies and South America quickly, yet got nowhere in Central America and points north. (*Note:* The type coming in with the slaves was probably the *Schistosoma mansoni* or intestinal variety. The snail in which it lives in Africa, known as *Planorbis boissyi* was present and abundant in South America. Although large numbers of infected African slaves were imported in the north, the proper snail was either not there or not there in large enough numbers to loose an epidemic.)

Wandering Bantu tribesmen carried the disease farther south and west in Africa. When the Bantus came, bilharziasis, coincidentally, was never far behind.

Dominique-Jean Larrey (1766-1842), the military surgeon to whom Napoleon (1769-1821) willed 100,000 francs because he was "the most virtuous man I have ever known," noted the bloody urine condition among French troops invading Egypt, 1799-1801.

In 1847 a ship carrying lacquer broke up near a Japanese fishing village close by Hiroshima. Its cargo spilled and literally painted the beach.

Later, rice farmers complained of eruptions of a kind they had never known on their hands and feet. They saw but one explanation. From then on the ricelands were called "Urishi." In Japanese this word means lacquer. The farmers believed the eruptions were caused somehow by the spilled lacquer. The disease was bilharziasis (of the Asiatic variety). Whether it was brought in by an infected crewman whose excrement found its way into the rice field waters was never made clear.

During this period of European colonialist expansion, troops posted to Africa, to Egypt in particular, were advised to wear penis sheaths and condoms while bathing in rivers. It was believed that small leeches bearing the disease bored into the urethra and caused the bleeding.

The bleeding was still generally considered to be the only consequence of this disease.

*   *   *

The history of bilharziasis yields little excitement as malaria does and little horror as leprosy does. Though it has contributed to deaths of millions since ancient days, it seldom kills by itself, and its most noticeable symptom, the bloody urine, is singularly unglamorous. Though one of the most prevalent and far flung ailments, it attracted the narrowest epidemiological interest over the centuries. In mid-19th century, its cause was still unknown. In fact, it did not even have a proper name.

Then, in 1851 Theodor Bilharz (1825-1862) determined the organism causing bloody excretions for centuries. In autopsy at Kasr el Aini Hospital in Cairo he rooted blood flukes from the mesenteric vein of a man who died suffering great blood loss.

The worm was named *Schistosoma haemotobium*, which loosely means "worm that lives in the blood." The latter word comes from the Greek *haima* (blood) and *bios* (life).

The disease, identified and described for the first time, was given its present name, bilharziasis. It was the vesical, or urinary variety and was thought at first to be the only form of bilharziasis.

The next major breakthrough was that of Patrick Manson (1844-1922). Manson, an inquisitive Scot in the Chinese Imperial Maritime Customs Service, sometimes performed autopsies in graveyards in studying tropical disease and left the orient with an impressive list of original observations and discoveries to his credit. Among them was his description of the eggs of intestinal bilharziasis in 1893. This type and the creature responsible for it now bear his name: Manson's bilharziasis, affecting the large bowel, caused by *Schistosoma mansoni*.

In 1904 in Japan Fujiro Katsurada found worms in cats and in so doing discovered the organism *(Schistosoma japonicum)* responsible for the third kind of bilharziasis (Asiatic) which infests the small intestine.

The history of bilharziasis since Manson and Katsurada is mainly one of research accomplishments:

1909—Two Japanese scientists showed conclusively that skin is the portal of infection. They also found man is not the only natural host preferred by *Schistosoma japonicum*. So are cattle, dogs, and cats. Possession of cats and dogs was discouraged. Horses replaced oxen as farm animals when it was discovered horse dung rarely contained any eggs. The government encouraged farmers to raise ducks in hope the fowl would eat and wipe out the snails.

1913—Unslaked lime and calcium cyanide were found deadly

to snails. This was perhaps the first demonstration of control measures against snail vectors.

1914—R. T. Leiper (1881-   ) proved *Schistosoma haematobium* and *Schistosoma mansoni* are transmitted by two different snails, *Bulinus contortus* and *Planorbis boissyi*, respectively.

1918—Tartar emetic was first prescribed as a bilharziasis cure in Khartoum, Sudan.

1919—Calcium oxide, otherwise called lime, was first used as a molluscicide. Live steam, hot water, and tidal salt water were also pumped onto snail beds in molluscicidal efforts. Salt water was an effective killer.

1929—Fuadin R proved effective intramuscular treatment in Cairo.

1944-1945—Bilharziasis broke out among Australian and American troops after Leyte Island invasion, Philippines, 1944.

1952—The first WHO assisted bilharziasis project began outside Cairo.

1953—Cementing walls of ditches in which snails breed was found good for killing snails. Cementing began in Japan.

1965—Research indicated transmission of *Schistosoma haematobium* and *Schistosoma mansoni* was broken with use of compounds developed on Egyptian control projects.

*   *   *

The research continues. Its findings are encouraging. Circumstantial but convincing evidence indicates one schistosome infection grants man immunity to subsequent infections. Radiological diagnostic equipment small and light enough for field use should be available soon. Several molluscicides deadly to snails but of no bother to food fish have been developed.

Where ambitiously applied, research findings and technology work. The bilharziasis control program in the United Arab Republic is an example: it was begun 50 years ago and is one of the oldest and most extensive in the world. With malaria now under control, bilharziasis is considered the country's first health problem. Egyptians harbor either vesical or Manson's bilharziasis. The current control phase, code named Egypt-49, labors in four areas: mass treatment, snail control, health education, sanitation. UAR spends $2,000,000 yearly on mass treatment, another $1,000,000 on snail control. The money is deemed well spent. The amounts are small; the return is enormous.

Economic loss to UAR from bilharziasis-caused work absentee-ism among 14,000,000 infectees is calculated at $560,000,000 yearly.

There is strong evidence Egypt-49 is accomplishing interruption of bilharziasis transmission in the Nile Valley, the result of chemical snail control. There is also an apparent fringe benefit. Some diseases affecting cattle are disappearing also.

Though the findings are encouraging, progress is not. Research workers build and build upon bilharziasis technology that gathers dust because there are just not enough skilled people in the field to apply it. Control, as a result, proceeds at the same speed of decades past, that is, slow in most places. Treatment with antimonial compounds, the present base of almost all schistosomal chemotherapy, sometimes suddenly kills patients. An end of bilharziasis is as yet a mirage.

*   *   *

Science and technology have not yet broken the hold of witch doctors and reasoned away superstitions no one will recant. The medicine men often forbid their neighbors to take drugs or control measures. The people often obey. It has been said that those in backward areas will accept modern treatment when well, but when really sick, they still seek out their faith and amulet healers. The jest is truth. Health authorities often must call police to enforce sanitation measures.

The witch doctors often do not have to urge resistance at all. Many sufferers never attend clinics, despite laws making treatment mandatory and penalizing refusal. Many who do attend do not complete the cure. Already drained of vitality by the time they begin treatment, they have no strength to move their bodies to clinics week after week. They also have little interest. Bilhaziasis has been among them so many centuries it is considered a part of life.

These attitudes present problems to strain the intuitiveness and persuasiveness of field workers to breaking, such as one described by Dr. C. W. Göckel of WHO's parasitic diseases section:

Natives of a New Guinea backwater were asked to submit urine samples. The sample colors ranged from pink to crimson, the classic bilharziasis sign.

When medication was suggested the men were puzzled. They were proud of their bloody urine; the bloodier, the better.

Reasoning: All men's urine was red. Therefore, all men's urine was supposed to be red. If blood did not appear by the time puberty ended, boys worried and their fathers sank into depression.

The first pinkish tinge was a sign of coming of age. Until it appeared, a boy was not a man.

PROFILE OF BILHARZIASIS:

Definition: A prolonged, enervating, often fatal disease (some consider it a group of diseases) caused by parasitic microorganisms commonly called blood flukes lodging in veins and resulting in uncomfortable gastro-intestinal or genito-urinary bleeding and upset. There are three major kinds:

1—Vesical (or urinary), affecting the urinary bladder primarily.

2—Manson's (or intestinal) attacking the large intestine.

3—Oriental (or Asiatic or Japanese), lodging in the small intestine.

Note: Bilharziasis is also called schistosomiasis. The oriental variety is most destructive of the three.

Symptoms: All three show sharply elevated count of certain white blood cells known as eosinophiles, large itchy reddish skin patches, late afternoon fevers, and tenderness of liver. Specifically:

1—Vesical bilharziasis produces bladder concretions or "stones," fibrosis of pelvic organs, granulomatous brain tumors, massive blood discharges in the urine.

2—Manson's shows itself by diarrhea, intestinal nodules, bloody urine, thickening of intestine to a degree *Encyclopedia Britannica* (v. 20 1964) describes as "the consistency of an old, nonelastic garden hose."

3—Oriental shows principally the same symptoms as Manson's. Chief discomfort of all bilharziases is a wrenching or tearing feeling inside. At some stage of development all blood flukes grow spines or "hooks" with which they anchor themselves to the vein wall against the blood flow. The tugging on these hooks causes the pain.

Fatality: Death results from extreme neglect, 12 per cent of all cases in some parts of South America.

Complications: Superimposed urinary tract infections and urinary obstruction is common in vesical bilharziasis. The intestinal form leads to liver cirrhosis and spleen enlargement.

Infectious agent: The schistosome, or blood fluke. Schistosomes belong to the trematodes, a group of the flatworm class (Platyhelminthes). Adult flukes are fragile worms a quarter inch to an inch long. Schistosome is a Greek-rooted word, from *schistos* meaning split, and *soma* meaning body. It pertains to the cleft along the male worm's body which houses the female worm while she lays her eggs. The relationship is sometimes a long one. Females sometimes lay for 25 years. Each major bilharziasis has its infecting agent:

1—Vesical bilharziasis is caused by *Schistosoma haematobium.*
2—Manson's, by *Schistosoma mansoni.*
3—Oriental bilharziasis, by *Schistosoma japonicum.*

Occurrence: *Schistosoma haemotobium* occurs in Africa, the Middle East, Portugal. There is some incidence in India. *Schistosoma mansoni* appears in Africa also, Arabia, northeastern and eastern South America and the Caribbean area. *Schistosoma japonicum* is oriental in focus as the name suggests. Schistosomes infect 200,-000,000 world wide. Bilharziasis is a tropical disease. Neither of the three species described above is indigenous to North America. Half the population is sometimes affected in endemic areas.

Reservoir: Man is the principal storehouse. Dogs, pigs, cattle, horses, rodents are other important hosts of *japonicum.*

Infection source: For all three major varieties, water contaminated with cercariae (larval forms of schistosomes) released by snails. The host snail of *Schistosoma haemotobium* is of genus *Bulinus*; of *mansoni*, genus *Planorbis*; of *japonicum*, genus *Oncomelania*. Snails suitable for one are not for the others.

Transmission: Eggs of *Schistosoma haemotobium* leave the human body mainly in urine, those of *mansoni* and *japonicum* in feces. The eggs hatch in water. Hatched larvae (called miracidia at this stage) enter snail host. After several weeks' growth in snail host, free swimming larvae (now called cercariae) emerge. The swimmers find an animal host, usually man, in the water, working or bathing. Larvae drill through the skin and into the bloodstream in 24 hours, using a tissue-cutting enzyme. They come to rest in the blood vessels of the liver and develop to maturity (females about an inch long). Then they migrate to the veins of their breeding place organ (bladder or intestines) choice depending upon species of worm. (See Definition above.) There they produce eggs which pass into a water source in urine or feces. The cycle begins again.

Portal of infection: Skin, as described above.

Incubation: Symptoms first appear four to six weeks after man is infected. Eggs appear in body wastes a week or two after onset of symptoms.

Communicability period: As long as eggs show in urine and feces, possibly 25 years, as stated. Infected snails discharge cercariae for several months.

Susceptibility: Universal. Both sexes, all ages. Adolescents and young adults are hardest hit.

Resistance: A debatable matter, but results of animal tests indicate man can possibly develop immunity.

Specific treatment: Antimonial drugs. For vesical and Manson's bilharziasis, FuadinR intramuscularly is widely used. For Asiatic, tartar emetic intravenously but with care. Toxic side effects appear. *Note:* A new, more effective drug was under test as of March, 1967.

Prevention: Five of the most important steps:

1—Keep human wastes from fresh water in which snail hosts live: ponds, irrigation ditches for example. Keep out animals infected with *Schistosoma japonicum*.

2—Attack snail breeding places with molluscicides.

3—Provide cercariae-free bathing and drinking water.

4—Provide wading boots, waterproof clothing for people entering known contaminated water.

5—Education. Persuade people in endemic areas to stay out of contaminated water if possible and stop dumping human wastes in.

Control: Report cases to local authorities. Arrange some sanitary disposal of feces and urine. Hunt the common source of infection: a lake, perhaps. Isolation and quarantine are unnecessary.

Basic public health measures during epidemics: Basically the same as described in Prevention above but on wide scale, with mass treatment of victims.

International measures: None practical or recommended.

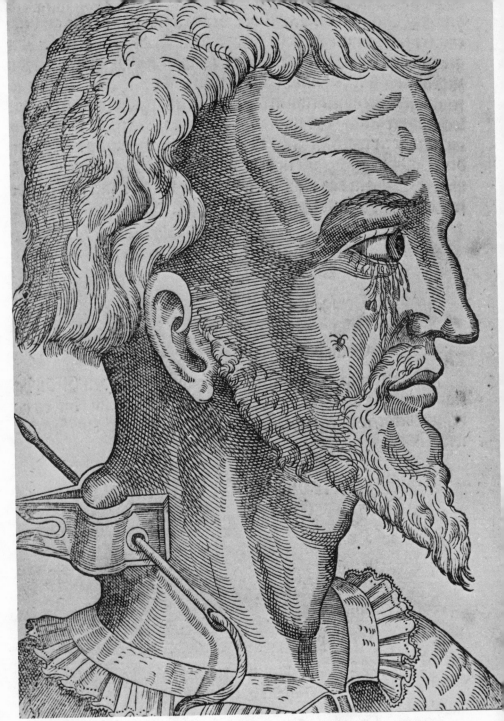

17th century Rx. For cure of eye diseases one treatise of this period recommended wicks (soaked in honey, vinegar, and verdigris) threaded through the eyelids. Also advised was a piercing of the neck, with a long threaded spike, a process known as "perforation"

World Health Organization

VII ONCHOCERCIASIS

". . . in the villages of the blind. . . ."

Onchocerciasis (or river blindness, or blinding filariasis, or buffalo gnat disease) is a criminal without a record.

Little can be said about it historically because its history is so short. There was no sharp clinical identification of it as an entity unto itself until 20 years ago.

Its seemingly sudden emergence in central Africa and South America would appear to make it another epidemiological mystery, that is, a new disease which suddenly appeared explosively from undetermined origins to darken the eyes of millions. If this were true, onchocerciasis would represent the fastest spreading holocaust in history.

It is not true. Onchocerciasis has caused blindness for centuries; its precise age is uncertain. The murky history is the result of mistaken identity. It was not recognized as a disease itself because it was mistaken so long for a symptom or manifestation of others in a broader category of infection known as filariasis.

WHO's parasitic disease unit states: "The present knowledge of the geographical distribution still suffers from the fact that onchocerciasis until very recently had not been recognized as an important cause of morbidity. Consequently, onchocerciasis was overlooked in many areas."

No more. Its sources, its personality, its manifestations, and its weak and strong points are well known and fairly well understood.

Nothing in this enlightenment has yet effectively reversed the course of onchocercal blindness, however. There are African villages in which most of the men beyond their early 20's are blind. For some reason yet to be fully fathomed, the disease strikes males harder than it does females. Young boys lead the blind in trains through their aimless days, each man holding the staff of another. The boys regard this depressing chore as putting something away for the future. One day they too expect to be blind and in need of boys to lead them when they take a place in the train.

109

The cause of onchocerciasis is a minute parasitic nematode worm *Onchocerca volvulus* which grows to about a millimeter in length, and is therefore visible without magnification but just barely.

The adult worms are most comfortable living in subcutaneous tissues, preferably those of man. Their genus name, *Onchocerca,* is derived from Greek as is customary in parasitic nomenclature. *Onkos* means barb. *Kerkos* means tail. *Onchocerca volvulus* in all its varieties has a hooked tail. The worms often create pockets or nodules in the skin where they live coiled up singly or in pairs.

The female worm discharges millions of young, called microfilariae, during her long life span. Many live 15 years inside the human skin. These microfilariae migrate through the body, establishing new pockets as they go. From pockets on the head, they eventually reach the eyes, burrow in, and begin their destruction by building cataracts and withering the optic nerve. The trip from nodules to the eyes may take seven years. This is normal time between first infection and first signs of eye damage.

Man passes the infection to man via a cooperative black fly with a fondness for human blood. The complete infection cycle is a complex series of man-fly-worm-man steps involving a larval stage in each man and fly host.

First clinical symptoms (itching, thickening and depigmentation of skin) appear slowly (as long as four months) and undramatically. Early diagnosis is thus often difficult.

The heaviest infection loads (determined by actual nodule count and other skin tests) in man are found in those who have suffered prolonged exposure to fly bites. They have been likened to tenements inhabited by worms endlessly producing the destructive microfilariae. These are the people with greatest damage to eyesight or no eyesight at all.

Onchocerciasis occurs in central Africa and Central and South America.

In Africa there are two epidemiologically different onchocercal forms:

1—The forest type: In jungle areas the endemic foci are sprawling but rarely connected to adjacent foci. They usually coincide with the outlines of river valleys. Clinical manifestations, eye lesions in particular, are mild compared to those marking the second ype, which is . . .

2—The savannah, or grassland, type: Its foci are small, limited to breeding sites. Black flies swarm extraordinarily thick. Transmission is seasonal. The infection is usually very severe with high blindness rate.

Of all the blinding diseases, onchocerciasis is the most virulent. It acts faster and on more people than any other does, trachoma included.

An oft-quoted four-year-long survey in 1956 in West Africa by the Royal Commonwealth Society for the Blind showed that 1,500 out of every 100,000 are blind in areas where onchocerciasis is endemic. By contrast the rate in Europe was only 250 blind in every 100,000 from all causes.

Onchocerciasis is largely a disease of river valleys; the rivers are favorite black fly breeding places. In the Volta River Basin alone incidence of onchocercal blindness is commonly ten per cent, often three times that in some villages. In this basin 100,-000 are sightless.

In the Sudan Republic, in the Bahr-el-Chazal and Equatorial provinces, Sudan Republic, 60 per cent of those infected had lesions growing in their eyes, and 5.6 per cent were blind.

A WHO survey in 1953 found 80 to 100 per cent infected in some African areas, before control measures and treatment.

The highest individual case loads anywhere today are borne by some Mexican villages: 75 per cent infected.

The effect on economy and future of endemic areas is lamentable. The parasitic diseases, however, seem to demand a still higher price. One reason is, a disease such as cholera appears in volcanic epidemic then peters out. It hopefully interrupts life and living only a short while, even though its toll may be high. The parasitic ones, prevailing all the time, represent constant emotional and financial extortion. Examples:

● Ghana—Mass blindness has reduced the output of already primitive farming to below survival level. Adult males who normally work the farms spend their days in dark idleness. They also eat, which means those not blind must share their food. Since one rarely dies from onchocerciasis itself, the ranks of the blind grow and remain a community burden while the numbers of the productive shrink.

● Uganda—A high infection rate drove the senior staff of a lumber region into rebellion. They quit. The mills closed. Uganda lost an important piece of its gross national product.

● Everywhere—The nuisance of fly bites hampers work to an enormous degree. Black flies are vicious biters. In one central African district it was estimated that field workers spent 15 minutes of every hour slapping flies. The remaining 45 minutes were almost a waste; a man constantly waiting to slap a fly does not work well.

The above illustrate the effect of onchocerciasis on economy and development. On the other side, economy and development can have an effect on onchocerciasis.

A new hydroelectric dam, for example, or an earthen dam for an irrigation project, can create additional fly incubators in their spillways. It was necessary on a west African dam job to spend $100,000 a year to protect the workers from onchocerciasis and other fly borne diseases. Workers on other projects simply walked off at first hint of the disease; they left their villages.

One assessment of this unanticipated development, in summer 1967, was harsh: "The benefits of economic expansion created by new irrigation and water conservation schemes will be greatly reduced if authorities neglect health aspects of such schemes," said Dr. N.A. Ansari, head of WHO's parasitic diseases unit.

❊   ❊   ❊

Prior to mid-19th century, onchocerciasis was not one of the great scourges. Then it suddenly seemed to leap to life. Today it is a disease of quiet but pandemic proportions. The most persuasive reason given for the eruption is the end to the slave trade.

It is the belief of many epidemiologists that millions of Africans had literally "taken to the hills" over the centuries, that is, they sought sanctuary from the slave gatherers in the ravines and crags of hills and mountains. In the cooler high altitudes there are no diseases such as onchocerciasis and malaria. These are diseases of the lowlands.

When slave hunting ceased, they migrated gradually downhill into the valleys to farm, and into the onchocerciasis belt.

Once more Africans are moving back to their hills. Their unflagging enthusiasm for escape creates further socio-economic problems within the epidemiological one.

*The miracle of faith. A 14th century
Ethiopian artist (name lost to us)
depicted Christ curing the blind.*
World Health Organization

1—Young women follow the fit young men: they are their future husbands. Together they represent all the able-bodied of both sexes in some districts. They leave behind entire villages of blind and old people who cannot care for themselves.

2—The logic of control and eradication efforts is apparent; if an area is onchocerciasis free, the able-bodied remain to work. They benefit and the country's wealth increases. Yet, public health workers find it difficult to convince governments to support control programs in areas from which people are fleeing.

※   ※   ※

Uganda believed and profited.

In a 1952 project, as described in a report by a WHO Expert Committee on Onchocerciasis (WHO Technical Report Series, No. 335, Geneva, 1966):

> . . . applications of DDT to the Victoria Nile in 1952 greatly reduced the numbers of *Simulium damnosum* (a genus of black fly) along the river over a distance of 72 kilometers in a region where the infection rate among river side dwellers was 99 per cent. In this instance, control operations were undertaken primarily to protect workers building the Owen Falls dam, both from the bites of *Simulium damnosum* and from onchocerciasis . . . with the alleviation of the biting scourge over 1,600 square miles there followed a spectacular uncapitalized development, and previously untenable land was transformed into a major producing area of food and cash crops. Surveys showed an increase in population of 164 per cent between 1948 and 1959, compared with only 19 per cent in neighboring unaffected areas, and there was also an appreciable rise in land values.

Kenya believed also and control programs killed or drove out onchocerciasis-bearing black flies by dosing rivers with insecticide. The flies still have not reinvaded. The cost was minuscule, $1.82 to $3.35 per square kilometer. Some areas demanded more effort than others, which accounts for the cost differential.

The black fly, of genus *Simulium*, which plays the role of intermediate host is an individualistic, hardy vector.

In Central and South America it works best between 750 and 1,500 meters altitude. Onchocerciasis was once considered an occupational hazard of coffee plantations. Most are located at this level.

The black fly is attracted to traps tagged with dark blue or black disks. It has no interest at all in yellow.

Certain species of black fly can distinguish between different animals and birds, as proven with dummys. Those preferring mammal blood landed on cow figures, those with liking for birds attacked winged figures, et cetera.

It has an extraordinary flight range, almost 50 miles. This helps account for its dry season survival. It can range far in search of water.

The fly deliberately submits its young to a rough-and-tumble birth by laying its eggs in fast-running water. It shows special fondness for dam spillways and waterfalls.

The *Simulium damnosum* dive into racing streams to attach egg clusters to vegetation or rock.

So many flies sometimes gang up at the same site that their clusters form masses as big as a man's fist and weigh a half-pound.

The female black fly generally needs a blood meal before laying eggs. A female biting a man in an experimental cage will lay sterile eggs. The eggs of a wild-caught female are fertile.

※　　※　　※

This ornery black fly is the subject of ambitious research.

Control of onchocerciasis (or any parasitic disease) is accomplished by one, breaking the transmission chain, or two, reducing the disease to a level at which it ceases to be a health problem.

The first involves taking some action against the vector.

The second involves chemotherapy, usually against the parasite in man.

The first method, control of the vector, in this case the black fly, is the most effective curb on onchocerciasis found so far. Drug therapy has been tried and found wanting. Its aim in onchocerciasis is to kill both adult worms and young microfilariae in the human host. The three drugs presently available do not always kill both, and the side reactions they can produce (gastritis, nausea, itching) are toxic. Their handling is complex and critical. Toxicity and complexity render them unfit for treatment of multitudes. There is extensive surgery in

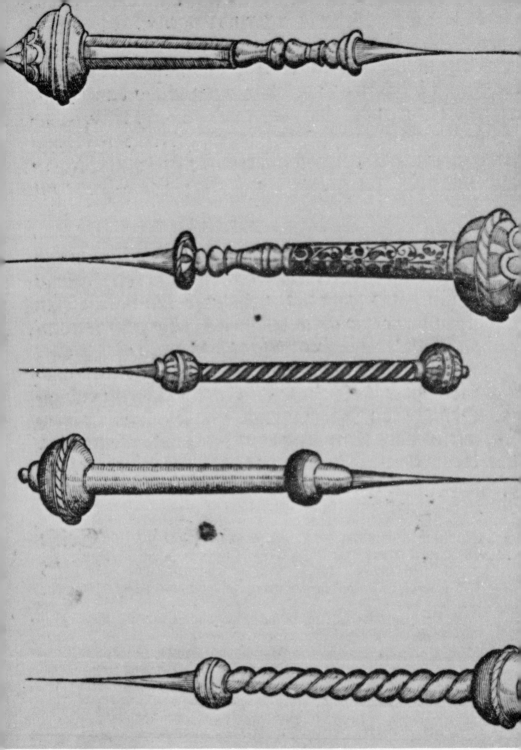

Instruments of healing. Sixteenth century eye probes of gold, used for removing cataracts.
World Health Organization

gross infection districts, sometimes 25 operations daily, but this is repair work on eye tissues rather than therapy.

Ground larviciding is the most energetic vector control form. The preferred formula is an emulsion containing 25 to 30 per cent DDT, applied to moving waters (rivers, spillways) at rates varying from .05 to 0.5 parts per million once every seven to ten days. The dose is enough to kill larvae but spares food fish. Dosing continues throughout the transmission season, sometimes for three months.

Aerial larviciding is popular fly control in Canada and the U.S. Two sprayings of DDT in fuel oil all but wipe out a breed of blackfly there. There are doubts that this would work on the onchocerciasis flies in Africa. Their larvae incubate under heavy forest canopies; the insecticide would probably not reach them.

Adulticides (compounds deadly to mature insects) have generally failed, mostly because they must be applied to adult flies while they rest. No one knows where they do this. Resting sites and habits are almost a complete mystery still.

At its easiest, vector fly control is a hard road to follow. The DDT spread is the least of it. Beforehand men must plot breeding sites, chop access points to rivers, truck insecticide and dispensing equipment through rains and mud troughs which pass for roads. Afterward they track the insecticide downstream to determine its reach, sometimes literally wading along with it.

Such programs are generally joint effort between international health organizations and nations where onchocerciasis is endemic.

Controlling flies remains difficult. To blame are lean funds and the discouraging shortage of trained staff that persists as the disease itself does. In jeopardy as result is the most ambitious onchocerciasis campaign to date, the Volta River Basin Pilot Control Project. This is a joint effort shared by Ghana, Upper Volta, Togo, and WHO. They share the most wearisome onchocerciasis problem in all Africa. One project objective is proof that coordinated operations involving more than one nation are practical and workable. So far they have not been so to any boastworthy degree.

Reluctance of nations sharing the disease to also share control have been as frustrating as lack of knowledge, money, and trained people.

Meanwhile. . . .

In central Africa entire villages now stand empty. The wells and squares belong to the wild animals, the houses belong to the wind. Everyone has gone to the hills above the "pest line" where they can live free of onchocerciasis and other diseases.

The men do return now and again, however, and when asked why, one replied, "To catch an occasional fish. There is no better spot in all of Africa for catching fish."

PROFILE OF ONCHOCERCIASIS:

Definition: A chronic, highly communicable, vector borne, body draining and often blinding infection caused by miniscule parasitic worms. Synonym: River blindness.

Symptoms: Visible skin nodules housing one or more coiled up worms and appearing anywhere on the body. Itchy skin. Mottled skin on front of calf, or shin. Acute dermatitis on back, buttocks, and thighs. Men and women both suffer thickening of genital skin. Men suffer mild scrotal swelling, or elephantiasis.

Note: Additional symptoms occur only in Guatemala and Mexico. They are: *Erisipela de la costa*, a severe fever producing dermatitis on the head. *Mal morado*, a facial and pectoral eruption coloring the skin purple. Leonine facial appearance due to sagging, atrophying skin.

Fatality: Few deaths can be directly attributed to onchocerciasis.

Complications: Enlarged lymph nodes on the groin, associated with loose atrophying skin folds drooping over them, bringing on a "hanging groin" condition.

Most serious complications are those of the eyes: cataracts, glaucoma, and ultimate loss of sight. These last occur when young worms, or microfilariae, travel along the lymphatic system to the eyes from above mentioned skin nodules. They can be seen with instruments in the cornea and eye fluid.

Infectious agent: Onchocerca volvulus, a nematode parasite worm. The female worm may live 15 years coiled in human skin nodules; during this time she discharges millions of microfilariae.

Occurrence: Onchocerciasis is most prevalent in central Africa along a belt extending from Sierra Leone on the west coast to

Ethiopia and Sudan in the east. Pockets exist in Venezuela, Columbia, Guatemala, and Mexico. WHO estimates 20,000,000 victims world wide, most in central Africa. Infection rate in some African locales is 80 per cent of the population, blindness rate 35 per cent.

Reservoir: Man.

Infection source: Certain black fly species of genus *Simulium,* small in size and vicious biters. *Simulium damnosum* is the source in most of Africa, with *Simulium neavei* in eastern and central Africa. In South and Central America, sources are *Simulium ochraceum, metallicum,* and *callidum.*

Transmission: When biting an already infected person the black fly vector sucks blood bearing *Onchocerca volvulus* microfilariae. After six days (in Africa) or 14 days (in Western Hemisphere) the microfilariae develop into infective larvae. The fly releases these the next time it stings a man to drink another blood meal, thus completing the life cycle of the parasite. Onchocerciasis is not transmitted from man to man.

Portal of infection: The human skin, via black fly, as described above.

Incubation: Nodules appear in three to four months. Female worms inside them begin larva discharge a year or more after the fly bites and infects the human.

Communicability period: Man is infectious as long as living *Onchocerca volvulus* microfiliariae are present in skin, up to 20 years as noted above.

Susceptibility: Universal.

Resistance: Little is known; some people appear more resistant than others. Studies are underway.

Specific treatment: Lance nodules and pull out worms (the process is called denodulization). Apply chemotherapy. Chemotherapy is limited. Its object is to kill both adult worms and microfiliariae in man. Present drugs do not do so satisfactorily.

Only three are effective:

1—Diethylcarbamazine: kills microfilariae but not worms, causes severe allergic reactions. Use is limited. Orally administered.

2—Suramin: Administered intravenously. Kills adult worms and many microfilariae but has limited mass use value because of high toxicity and need for careful supervision.

3—Mel-W (trimelasan): Intramuscular injection. Kills worms but leaves microfiliariae. Objections to use are the same as above.

Prevention: Cover body as much as possible, use insect repellent to avoid *Simulium* bites. Dose larvae in swift running streams with DDT. Dose adult flies also if possible. Establish centers for diagnosis and treatment.

Control: Of patients and contacts, very little control is possible, except for reporting new cases to health authorities. Isolation, concurrent disinfection, and quarantine are not necessary. There is no known immunization. Treat patients in manner described above.

Epidemic measures: Basically the same as preventive measures above.

International measures: multilateral action by countries where disease is endemic to kill flies and larvae, prevent migration of infectees across boundaries, and treat infectees at such boundaries.

VIII PLAGUE

"... ashes, ashes...."

Ring around the rosy,
A pocket full of posies,
Ashes, ashes,
All fall down....

—Updated version of medieval English children's doggerel. The line "Ashes, ashes," was originally something like "achoo, achoo," representing the sneezes of victims in final throes of plague.

Slaughter of innocents. The medievals believed certain people spread plague purposely with evil intent, held this to be a criminal act, and burned at the stake those accused of doing so, as shown in this old woodcut.

Plague (or pest, or oriental plague) is another ancient illness; it appeared in time perhaps farther back than appearance of either rat or man. The disease was a certain possibility at least as far back as the Paleolithic Period. The rat is one of the plague bacillus' hosts. Rat skeletons have been found in caves inhabited by men in Israel 25,000 years ago.

The first recorded plague outbreak is generally conceded to be the one which bedeviled the Philistines in 1320 B.C., a punishment for stealing the Hebrews' Ark of God. It is described in the fifth chapter of 1 Samuel in the Holy Bible as "emerods in their secret parts. . . ." Chapter six, same book, states, ". . . for one plague was on you all, and on your lords."

Emerods were probably plague buboes, the egg size swellings of plague infection sites, that is, if the scourge mentioned in 1 Samuel was indeed plague. (See Symptoms, profile at end of chapter.) The word "emerods" is probably precursor of the current word "hemorrhoid."

North Africa knew the plague well in pre-Christian times; North Africa in fact was considered its home. Asiatic Indians knew of it too, with a misty notion that rats somehow caused the disease. The *Bhagavata Purana*, a fifth century medical work, warns people to flee their homes "when rats fall from the roofs above, jump about and die." They died from plague, presumably.

Plague, a disease definitely plague, has flooded the earth periodically since the Philistines, peaking without notice in pandemic waves, then ebbing, also without notice, for reasons still not understood. This secret of epidemiology is not better kept by any other disease. Henry E. Sigerist (1891-1957), who brightened and broadened medical history by his humanistic approach to it, said, "We know the bacillus that causes plague, and we know how it is transmitted from rodents to man, and how an epidemic spreads along the highways of traffic. Yet we do not know why Europe was devastated by two pandemics of plague in the sixth and 14th centuries, but experienced no serious outbreak of the disease during the intervening 800 years, although Europe had very close and intimate contacts with the Orient during the crusades."

There have been three distinct plague pandemics since the indistinct Philistinic emerods. The third brought the infection to the U.S. and wild rodents are plague-ridden in Arizona, California, Colorado, and New Mexico, with occasional human cases; and civilians in South Vietnam where disease and war are once more proving inseparable mates.

The first pandemic was the bubonic variety (see Definition, profile at end of chapter). The disease flared up in 540 during the reign of the Byzantine Roman Emperor Justinian and is named the Plague of Justinian for this coincidence. Two possible places of origin: lower Egypt and/or Ethiopia.

This plague lasted 50 to 60 years and was a leveler equal to any imaginable nuclear holocaust. The English historian Edward Gibbon (1773-1794) estimated in his weighty *The Decline and Fall of the Roman Empire* that 100,000,000 dead was a figure "not wholly inadmissible." The plague leapt, as another chronicler said, "to the ends of the hospitable world," beginning at the seaports and radiating inland.

The historian Procopius (date unattainable) observed much dying during Justinian's plague. His description of the ugliness and agony is vivid and clinically meticulous. From his *De Bello Parsico:*

> They were taken with a sudden fever: some suddenly wakened from sleep; others while they were occupied with various matters during daytime. The fever, from morning to night, was so slight that neither the patients nor the physician feared danger, and no one believed that he would die. But in many even on the first day . . . a bubo appeared both in the inguinal regions and under the armpits. . . . Some died at once, others after many days, and the bodies of some broke out with black blisters the size of a lentil. These did not live after one day, but died at once, and many were quickly killed by a vomiting of blood. . . . Physicians could not tell which cases were light and which severe, and no remedies availed.

Between 5,000 and 10,000 died daily in Constantinople. The unburied were hooked from the streets by body gatherers and interred wholesale in whatever ways were handy. Some were dumped in mass graves outside the city. Others were stacked aboard ships and floated away on the outgoing tide.

This historian Procopius observed the living as well as the dead. He noted thievery, corpse looting, rape, landgrabbing, sexual orgies shared by people so desperate they no longer

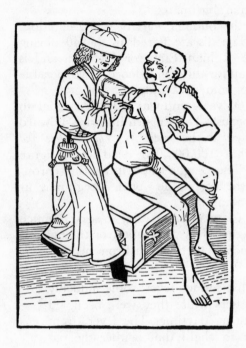

An antiplague measure. A barber physician lancing the boil of a bubonic plague victim. A 15th century woodcut.

cared how they behaved. To him "it seemed as though the disease had left only the most wicked."

The second pandemic was the Black Death which sowed corpses across Europe and Asia for three centuries. It first appeared in central Asia, in what is now the Kirghiz Soviet Socialist Republic in 1338 and 1339.

This remarkably precise determination was made by the Russian archeologist D. A. Chwolson (1819-1911) who found three medieval headstones there bearing inscriptions stating the persons interred were plague victims. The dates: 1338 and 1339.

He also noted an exceptionally large number of graves dated those same years, indicating some vast epidemic had been rampant.

From central Asia it infected Crimean seaports. From there it shipped to the Mediterranean. The first rat with infected fleas on its back possibly landed in Sicily in 1347 (See Transmission, profile at chapter end).

During the first great pandemic cycle in the 14th century, the plague received the name Black Death because subcutaneous hemorrhages darkened the skin of the dying. This indicates plague of septicemic variety (see Symptoms, end profile). The name more or less held over the next three centuries.

A quarter of Europe's population died during the first 14th century cycle, supposedly 25,000,000. The estimate of Pope Clement VI (1291-1352) was higher: exactly 42,836,486. More than 200,000 European villages and towns were reported drained of all souls by death. Millions died in Asia.

As the disease exploded like a walking barrage across Europe, it again seemed to leave "only the wicked."

One Johannes Nohl (1882-   ), himself a witness of a later plague epidemic, described in *The Black Death* how the public gravediggers recruited from jails and galley ships during the 14th century

> . . . penetrated the houses of the healthy, and drag-ged husbands, wives, and children to the plague hos-pital if they were refused money. . . . From all coun-tries it is reported that the gravediggers threw infected matter from their carts so as to stimulate the epidemic which for them was a time of luxury. . . .

Each faced Black Death in his own way. Some found com-fort in the Holy Bible. Others found in it license for gluttony, drunkenness, sexual promiscuity, and perversion. In the telling of how Jerusalem reveled just before the attack by Sennacherib. The Book says in part, "Let us eat and drink, for tomorrow we die."

History's scapegoats, the Jews, were set upon by panicked mobs and accused of every manner of plague spreading such as poisoning wells and black magic. The nobles, who almost universally owed something to Jewish bankers (money lending was one of the few pursuits allowed them), found it profitable to let the lynchings go on. Jews were thrown live into holes, covered with wood, and burned. In Mayence (now Mainz, Germany) 12,000 leapt into or were prodded into the fires. In Strassburg (now Strasbourg, France) 2,000 were accused of plague spreading and hanged at the Jewish cemetery.

So many died at Avignon in France that Pope Clement VI consecrated the Rhone River so the dead could be floated off.

The Ravens, as the gravediggers were named, could not shovel pits fast enough. The pope himself was at Avignon.

Jews were not the only lynch victims. In Milan in 1630 the commissioner of health himself was seized, dismembered, torn open with red hot pincers, fractured, racked for six hours, and finally roasted to death. The reason: He was seen wiping ink-stained fingers on the walls of a house while walking one day. Neighborhood women swore he was smearing plague on their homes.

The last great outbreak considered part of this second pandemic was the Great Plague of London, 1664-65. The atrocities then were as brutal as those during the 325 years preceding. The remedies were as futile: Flaming aromatics to clear the air of the "plague miasma." Perfumed water on clothing for the same purpose; today's eau de Cologne was originally a plague water. Laxatives.

The doctors protected themselves by wearing head to toe leather cassocks, gloves, and masks with glass eyepieces and a "stork bill" breathing snout, stuffed with fumigant-soaked air filters. They took pulses with wands to avoid touching the afflicted.

The Great Fire which burned most of London in 1666 is said to have ended the Great Plague, and the second pandemic too, except for occasional subsequent small flashes. To an extent this is true for London because so many plague bearing rats were incinerated. It was not necessary to burn down other cities to blot out plague, however. It just disappeared.

Plague expanded the technology of germ warfare. In 14th century sieges generals loaded bodies of plague dead into their catapults and hurled them into each others' cities. But otherwise, the lessons learned in 325 years were slight.

Three centuries after Black Death first appeared, there were still no cures and doctors in London offered feeble jokes in their place. Their best remedies, they said, were "three adverbial pills named quick, far, and late." This meant get out of the city quickly, go far, and return late to avoid the disease.

When rats died in the streets or fell convulsing from the rafters, plague followed. This much the ancient Indians knew. Any connection between rat and plague beyond that was unseen, however. That rats died of plague, which fleas then carried to man in the absence of rats, does not seem to have been clear.

The plague doctor. This was standard horror show costume
until the 17th century. The "birdbill" held filtering cloths.
The stick was used to feel pulses of infectees.

Museum des Vundervollen

Not all that was obvious was overlooked, however.

Quarantine was appreciated, and eventually applied through-out Europe though no one really understood it. In 1374 the Venetian Republic, remembering bitterly its own swift decima-tion in 1348, passed laws requiring all ships from infected areas to wait in the harbor roads for *quaranti giorni* (40 days) before landing. The reasoning was, plague aboard would have time to appear and burn itself out. The period became known as *guar-antena,* or quarantine.

The plague killed more than people. Its first cycle in the 14th century killed, or at least applied the first axe to, the fuedal system.

As landowners died serfs and craftsmen were left without masters. As serfs and craftsmen died, a labor shortage appeared which gave the survivors value and independence they never knew. As people saw their priests die as they themselves did, they lost faith in the church. The church lost some of its grip on the people.

Nothing in Europe was ever the same again.

*   *   *

Two hundred years passed plague free but for occasional hotspots.

Then, in 1855, the Moslems of Yunnan province in China revolted. The Chinese government sent in troops to suppress them. Epidemic broke out during the suppression. When the troops returned home, they carried plague with them.

This was how the third pandemic began.

The third covered more land area and embraced more coun-tries than either of the two previous plagues in its flow. This time it included the U.S.

The only bright event in this phase of plague's dismal history was discovery and identification in Hong Kong in 1894 of the plague-causing organism, the bacillus *Pasteurella pestis.* Two bac-teriologists get the credit, the Swiss Alexandre Yersin (1863-1943) and the Japanese Shibasaburo Kitasato (1852-1931). They made the final rat-flea-rat linkup, finding man is only the flea's second choice as food, but a choice which has resulted in all plague epidemics. When the plague kills rats, the flea must seek another feeding ground. This is invariably man. (See Transmis-sion, profile at chapter end.)

Plague has killed approximately 13,000,000 more since then, most in India and most between 1896 and 1917. Since 1917 the death rate has dropped like a stone. Examples: In 1907, the maximum death year of the third pandemic, 1,315,892 succumbed. In 1923 there were 250,000 deaths. In 1942, even with a world war, there were 10,577. Antibiotics, militant rat control, international sanitary regulations are responsible for most of the reduction.

*   *   *

In one sense, man has at best a discouraging 50-50 chance to control and/or destroy the rat. For every man alive, there is at least one rat, probably more.

Most countries have carried on active rodenticide for several decades. Taiwan paid bounties on 7,000,000 tails in 1959 and said the true kill that year was probably 30,000,000 rats. Total rats killed since 1894 conceivably run into billions.

Yet the world rat population remains about the same as that of man. India, with 472,000,000 people as of 1967 estimates its rats and other rodents total ten times its population figure, or 4,800,000,000. In the United States the odds are better, 100,000,000 to 195,000,000 humans.

Female rats can drop six litters yearly. There are up to ten young per litter. The average female then can breed 60 new rats every 12 months. One pair of rats could theoretically produce 20,000,000 descendants within three years at the conservative figure of three litters annually.

In world wide rat control efforts, WHO sponsors vector control research, serves as an information clearning house, shares surveillance duty with the UN Food and Agriculture Organization, organizes field trials of both rodenticides and insecticides. Many nations and organizations are approaching rat control along WHO lines.

In rat control the worst enemy is not always the rat.

The Citizen's Health Committee found San Francisco openly hostile to any suggestion of it in the year 1908. Admission that the Bay City harbored rats carrying plague might have driven international shipping from the port, and ruined its economy.

The police arrested a federal agent trying to make an inspection. The mayor threatened to fire four health board members who insisted plague was present in the Bay City. Docking and shipping interests filled the air with diversionary propaganda. For example:

Only people who ate rice caught plague.

No one who used soap regularly caught plague.

Plague could not infect anyone because pipes vented sewer odors into the atmosphere, a statement patently a resurrection of the miasma theory of disease.

Eighteen months later, however, the city was all but rat free, and was operating one of the world's best rat control programs.

It still is.

PROFILE OF PLAGUE:

Definition: Plague is a term once applied to any epidemic communicable disease bringing high mortality. It now refers only to one fulminating, flea or air borne, highly fatal infectious, bacillus caused, feverish disease. A widely used synonym is: bubonic plague. This is a misnomer. Bubonic plague is but on the disease's three clinical forms:

1—Bubonic plague, the most common, in which the infection sometimes enters the lungs, setting stage for . . .

2—Pneumonic plague, which devastates the lungs, and is rarer than bubonic.

3—Septicemic plague. This form shows no bubonic or pneumonic forms and is so virulent, death comes within hours.

Ironically, plague (the name embraces all three above) is essentially a disease of rodents, rats most usually. The infective bacillus prefers rodents to man and moves from one animal to the other via fleas. Man enters the rat-flea exchange accidentally. Only pneumonic can be passed from man to man. (See Transmission below.)

When plague occurs in cities it is sometimes called murine (rat) plague. In rural areas the infection is sometimes designated as sylvatic (woodland) or campestral (field) plague.

Symptoms: It is axiomatic that any mild attack is sure to be of bubonic variety. Three quarters of all plague cases are bubonic and some victims do indeed suffer only mild aggravation and recovery easily. Mild cases are comparatively rare. Attack is usually violent. Symptoms of each variety are:

1—Bubonic: Abrupt onset. Chills followed by fevers soaring as high as 107°F. Vomiting. Headaches commonly described as "splitting." Delirium, speech thickness, and lopsided gait, all conveying an impression of drunkenness. Burning sensation in the eyes. Tongue swollen and covered with white fur-like deposit. Diarrhea, a grave sign when it appears. Golf ball size buboes appear on the groin or in armpits on the second or third day at the sites of flea bites. Buboes are lymph glands swollen with infective material, usually on one side of the body only. (The adjective "bubonic" comes from bubo.) The swellings cause pain described as tearing, agonizing, exquisite. Untreated buboes form pus, burst, and sometimes hemorrhage.

2—Pneumonic: When bubonic infection attacks lungs, a form of pneumonia sets in. In addition to some or all bubonic symptoms, the victim also exhibits: gasping, rapid breathing, sometimes 60 breaths/minute. Darkening face, blood sputum, lungs eventually flood.

3—Septicemic: Usually only prostration, mental disorientation, high temperatures, and unconsciousness.

Recovery from all three forms is slow. Second attacks seldom follow within the same illness, but no immunity develops. *Note:* Where a rare occurrence, plague is frequently mistaken for other diseases, malaria and typhus in the tropics, for example.

Fatality: High. Bubonic, commonest and gentlest, kills 25 to 50 per cent of untreated cases in two to six days after onset. Untreated pneumonic and septicemic cases are almost 100 per cent fatal, pneumonic in three or four days, septicemic in two. Recovery from septicemic is rare in any event, treated or not.

Complications: Simultaneous bacterial infections.

Infectious agent: A rod-shaped bacillus linked end to end in pairs and chains, *Pasteurella pestis*. The organism is also called *Bacillus pestis* or *Yersinia pestis*, after Alexandre Yersin, one of its discoverers.

Occurrence: Plague appears anywhere rodents live. Unchecked, it is potentially a world wide, all climate disease. Urban or murine plague has been controlled in much of the world. Sylvatic plague still appears in western U.S., and is wide spread in South America and southern Africa. Also it is endemic in pockets in the Near East and central Asia, the latter an ancestral home.

Reservoir: Wild rodents, including ground squirrels. Infection may be transferred to domestic rats in city or country areas where domestic rats and wild rodents have contact. The rat is but a link in plague between wild rodents and man, not the source or reservoir as is commonly believed.

Infection source: Of bubonic, an infective flea. Of pneumonic, sputum of infectees, or droplets sprayed into the air by sneezes, even ordinary exhalation. Of septicemic, infective flea also.

Transmission: A rodent-flea-rodent chain, for each kind as follows:

1—Bubonic: A flea bites an infected rodent, sucks up plague organisms with its blood meal. Organisms start multiplying in the flea's stomach. Days pass. The organisms are prolific; there are now so many they clog the flea's stomach entrance in gelantinous masses. The flea is then known as "blocked" because it cannot draw blood into its stomach when it bites another victim. Elastic recoil of its gullet squirts blood, now bearing some infective bacilli back into the wound, as many as 24,000 per regurgitation. If the new victim being bitten is susceptible, bubonic plague sets in.

2—Pneumonic: This is transmitted from person to person by contact or by air-borne route from terminal bubonic patients developing pneumonic conditions.

3—Septicemic: Same as bubonic, except that the bacilli go directly into the blood. Bubonic and pneumonic symptoms do not appear. Septicemia (from which comes the adjective "septicemic") is the name given the infections commonly known as "blood poisoning." A plague victim's blood is poisoned in a sense by a massive invvasion of bacilli which reproduce quickly when injected directly into the nourishing stream.

The classic flea vector is *Xenopsylla cheopis*, of the family *Pulicidae*. It can transmit bubonic type of plague from animal to animal, animal to man, and man to man. Flea vectors prefer rodents. Man enters their relationship only by default. As rats die in plague time the fleas seek new animals on which to feed and live. If no suitable substitute rodents are present, the new animal is man. *Note:* Crushing fleas between the teeth as soldiers were once wont to do may cause an infection called tonsillar plague. Also, people have attempted murder using infective fleas as weapons.

Portal of infection: The skin or mucosa.

Incubation: Same times as listed under fatality.

Communicability period: Fleas remain infected sometimes for weeks. Blocked fleas, however, die within four days of blockage. Pneumonic is the only variety transmitted directly from man to man.

Susceptibility: General. All ages and both sexes.

Resistance: Infection grants only slight and temporary immunity. Vaccination with killed *Pasteurella pestis* affords six months immunity. Vaccination with virulent strains immunize for a year.

Specific treatment: Streptomycin, tetracycline, chloramphenicol, and sulfonamides. They work only if administered within first 24 hours.

Prevention: Vaccinate travelers entering, and residents of, endemic places. Trap and destroy rats. Ratproof buildings, docks, ships, warehouses. Fumigate cargoes from known plague areas.

Control:

1—Report all cases to health authorities (required by International Sanitary Regulations).

2—Hospitalize all patients, especially late pneumonic ones.

3—Disinfect clothing, wastes, and sputum discharges of all patients.

4—Quarantine all patients' contacts six days. Read temperatures every four hours and initiate drug therapy at first sign of rise. Do not immunize contacts. Concentrate on quarantine, close observation, drug therapy.

5—Fumigate suspected endemic neighborhoods with residual insecticides. Pursue antirat measures cited in prevention category.

Basic public health measures during epidemics:

1—Investigate all deaths to determine cause. Perform autopsies where necessary to confirm plague cases. Find and treat as many contacts as possible.

2—Start flea fumigation in widening circles with disease foci as centers. Follow with rat control.

3—Medicate all personnel exposed to plague risk. Quarantine medical people with pneumonic cases if possible.

4—Protect field workers from fleas with DDT powdering daily.

5—Vaccinate populations with a virulent bacillus vaccine.

International measures:

1—Governments should notify WHO and neighbor states of new cases and newly discovered or reactivated foci.

2—Enforce International Sanitary Regulations on deratting, flea killing, and fumigation of all transport from plague areas. These measures apply to ships especially. Dose ships with insecticide and rat poisons every six months.

3—Keep out travelers from plague countries. Keep in suspected plague victims and contacts. Travelers should immunize just before entering risk areas.

IX SMALLPOX

"The patient becomes a dripping, unrecognizable mass of pus. . . ."

There are three important dates in the history of every communicable disease: the date causal organism is unmasked, the date immunization is developed, the date cure emerges. They arrive at no determinable order in history and each is as important to mankind as the others. Cure sometimes proves the most elusive of all and last to appear.

There are still several brutal diseases for which no remedy is known. Smallpox is one. The infective organism (a virus called variola) has been identified. Effective immunization has been practiced for two centuries. There is as yet no known cure or treatment, however.

Once smallpox' attack begins the victim can only endure it. He can be comforted to a degree but nothing can be done to alter the onslaught. At some point he will recover, or he will become one of the average four in every ten who die from it.

Brutal is too small a word for smallpox. Dr. Archibald Hoyne, a knowledgable U.S. expert on contagion who died in 1963, once described its savagery thus: "The patient often becomes a dripping, unrecognizable mass of pus by the seventh or eighth day of eruption. . . . The putrid odor is stifling, the temperature often high, and the patient frequently in a wild state of delirium."

The *WHO Handbook for Smallpox Eradication Programs in Endemic Areas* contains this dark description of a typical case of variola major in its later stages:

> . . . Lesions continue to develop over the first eight days or so involving progressively the forearms and hands, upper legs, lower legs and feet. . . .
>
> Lesions also develop on the mucous membranes of the mouth and the palpebral conjunctiva . . . bringing corneal ulceration and sometimes blindness.
>
> By the tenth day of the illness, lesions become . . . flattened and velvety, hot and tender to the touch.

135

Local hemorrhage into the skin may occur. Great loss in weight becomes evident. By the 12th or 13th day, if the rash is extensive, large amounts of epidermis begin peeling away, particularly over pressure areas, leaving these areas painfully tender to the touch. . . . In fatal cases, death commonly occurs between the eighth and 15th day, apparently as a result of overwhelming toxemia, general intoxication, or because of hemorrhage. In general, it would appear that the more extensive the rash, the higher the fatality rate.

The dead and the dying. A drawing from the time of a Mexican smallpox plague in 1538. Corpses are arranged in the center. Two new diseased victims appear at right.
Bibliotheque de Geneve

Some of smallpox' other grim truths are:

It is possibly the most communicable of all diseases; some epidemiologists say it is positively so. Other diseases need a vector, or are seasonal, or can only be transmitted by direct contact, or in drinking water. All smallpox requires is a breath and the variola virus is blown from one mouth to another. It can be carried by articles touched by the victim, persons visiting him, and even by his body after death. Dr. Donald Henderson, WHO's Smallpox Eradication chief, once stated: "It is the most lethal disease and has the greatest spread potential of any disease in any country, any climate, any altitude, any person." (See Symptoms, Fatality, profile at chapter end.)

No one is born immune. To become immune, one must either be infected or be vaccinated at some time.

Also. . . .

Smallpox is erroneously believed by the public to be curable; curability is a false impression created today by its rarity. It is so rare that most doctors in the U.S. have never seen smallpox first hand.

Smallpox' murderous threat and capability are not extinct. Forty per cent of the unvaccinated victims died during outbreaks in England and Sweden in 1962 and 1963, despite fine medical care.

"Without a cure available to us, one case is still considered an emergency. We'll fly thousands of miles to investigate it," Dr. Henderson said in October, 1967, with good reason. With such virtuosity for contagion, one case in an unvaccinated population can loose an epidemic. Epidemic anywhere is bad news everywhere because of smallpox' easy spread.

"Reintroduction of the disease into the nonenedemic countries is feared, and with good cause," the 1967 *WHO Smallpox Eradication Handbook* stated. Smallpox has pushed mankind to the brink of extinction several times in the past.

*　　*　　*

The past once again begins in antiquity. Bumps on the mummy face of 11th century B.C. Egyptian Pharoah Ramses V bear sharp likeness to pox scars.

Shielding people from a disease by infecting them with the disease is one of medicine's soundest practices, and one of its oldest. Immunization was literally ancient when the 18th century breakthroughs in vaccination took place.

One of the Vedic books, authorship roughly dated 1200 B.C., describes inoculation, probably for smallpox:

> . . . put fluid from the pustules on to the point of a needle, and introduce it into the arm, mixing the fluid with the blood. A fever will be produced, but this illness will be very mild, and need inspire no alarm.

Historians of medicine and disease agree more or less that a certain pestilence resembling smallpox blew over Arabia sometime in the sixth century. Then it gradually spread along the Mediterranean ship and wagon routes, the traditional infiltration trails of disease, and into Europe east of Rome.

Written evidence of its existence remains circumstantial. For example, a siege of Mecca in 569 was supposedly relieved when large birds scattered showers of pebbles, each no bigger than a pea, over the besiegers. The pebbles adhered to their skins and the following day they were dead. For another example, in 570, Marius, Bishop of Avenches (532-596), described a grotesque skin disease which he called "variola," from Latin *varius* meaning "spotted." This is one of the first labels given smallpox and the most commonly used one today. There is little in such writing upon which to base a conclusive smallpox diagnosis, though the disease probably was smallpox.

The first reasonably accurate and clinically recognizable smallpox description is Persian, with parallel Latin translation, by the physician Abu El Razi Rhazes (860-932), a clinician ranked with Hippocrates, Aretaeus, and later the Englishman Thomas Sydenham (1624-1689). Rhazes made classic notes on the main symptoms and pustules (See Symptoms, profile at end of chapter) sometime near the year 900. He was convinced it was normal for children to contract this spotted disease. He reasoned that their blood was like new wine which must ferment and age.

Smallpox was a late starter. There were no pandemics in these early centuries and the epidemics wee small compared to the ragings of plague from Africa and the Orient. Slowness with which men traveled in those times accounts for laziness of spread. A voyager from the Levant, if infected with smallpox, either died or passed the infective stage by the time he reached Europe.

The Saracens brought it into Spain about the time the Persian Rhazes was practicing. The crusaders carried it home from their holy wars, passing it to one another on the way home as relay runners pass batons.

Smallpox was widely noted during the Middle Ages in England, but writers were stingy with figures; there is little with which to plumb prevalence in these times. The end of the medieval period seems to be the beginning of greater, near-epidemic spread, though smallpox was viewed as a children's disease. Girolamo Fracastoro (1484-1533), the farsighted scientist and physician noted for his beard and poetry and philosophy as well as his futuristic medical thinking on syphilis among other things, erred on smallpox. He too regarded it as an affliction of children, basically mild, but one to which everyone was susceptible.

There was no further mistaking smallpox' hellish temperament for childish affliction when it arrived in the New World with the Spanish fleets early in the 16th century. One of Hernando Cortez' (1485-1547) slaves was reported sick with it when they landed.

Whether it arrived in the body of one slave or bodies of other sick men later is not important. What happened within a few subsequent years is important. It illustrates why to this day the one or few fulminating cases loose among an unvaccinated population are so dreaded.

Three and a half million died of smallpox in Mexico and Central America. Thus, once more a disease played an historic role. Smallpox served as a colonizing force. It certainly did what the comparatively few Spanish men and few Spanish cannon could not have done as easily as they did, that is, weaken and demoralize Aztec rule and Aztec society. This is not to say there would have been no conquest of Mexico without smallpox, only that without smallpox, the conquest would have been much more difficult.

Without it the personal lives of historical figures would have been easier. In France it so disfigured the nose of King Charles IX (1550-1574) he appeared to have two of them.

※ ※ ※

Smallpox made its way north, infected the American Indian tribes of the temperate climates and killed half those it touched.

The Narragansetts of Massachusetts were all but annihilated. In 1633 they numbered 40,000. An epidemic reduced them to a few hundreds. The forests were described as being littered with bodies as numerous as fallen pine cones.

Some saw good in this ruination of an entire people. Reverend Cotton Mather (1663-1728), loudest voice of puritanism and witch hunting, said, "The Indians in these parts had newly, even about a year or two before, been visited with such a prodigious pestilence, as carried away not one tenth but nine parts of ten (yea 'tis 19 of 20) among them; so that the woods were almost clear of these pernicious creatures to make room for a better growth."

Some saw a germ warfare lesson in the Indian epidemics. Men planning war on the Indians several times first gave them blankets of pox victims, knowing the Indian fondness for warm cloth and knowing such blankets carried contagion. There was often no need to war at all; the disease slaughtered as effectively as muskets.

The practice was risky, for white men who handled the blankets were themselves prey to infection. Such gifts were discouraged, according to one account, by Indians who swaddled one of these generous colonials in his own contagious blankets and tied him to a stake until he contracted smallpox and died.

The disease became known in France as *le petite verole*, to distinguish it from *la grande verole*, which was the term for syphilis. The term "small pox" (a literal translation of *petite verole)* came into use for the first time in 16th century England. The Germans called it *Blattern*, also once used to designate syphilis.

England's first great smallpox epidemic engulfed Elizabethan London in 1628, and this particular outbreak is taken sometimes as one of the precursors to a pestilence then commencing a slow but enveloping contagion of all Europe.

Unlike plague, which flattened those who lived in squalor more than those who lived in wealth, pox displayed no prejudices. It infected everyone. One in four victims died during the 17th century throughout the world, 60,000,000 in Europe alone.

Half the population of Europe bore pox scars on their faces, "making the eyes and cheeks of the betrothed maidens objects of horror to the lover," according to Thomas Macaulay (1800-1859) writing of smallpox two centuries later.

Eighteenth century smallpox was hardly gentler:

1707. Iceland . . . 18,000 died of smallpox. Total population of Iceland that year was 50,000.

Same year. Paris . . . 14,000 died.

1721. Boston . . . The English ship *Sea Horse*, out of Barbados, brought one single case. Within weeks, 5,984 had taken the disease, and 894 died. This was Boston's sixth epidemic.

1730. Greenland . . . In this isolated place the Eskimoes were stricken. Sickness and fatality were untallied, but great.

1770. India . . . 3,000,000 died.

1776. U.S. . . . More than half of the 10,000-man revolutionary Continental Army of George Washington (1732-1799) was ill and unfit for duty that June. Most suffered smallpox.

1782. Italy . . . By one estimate nine Italians in every ten had smallpox that year.

※   ※   ※

The first major date in the western history of smallpox falls in the 18th century, namely, development of safe, effective immunization, and it is difficult to credit any one individual with all the work. Many practiced it, some making crusading social contribution, some scientific, most at great personal cost.

Inoculation in the ancient far eastern manner was the prevailing antismallpox measure. It involved rubbing a superficial scratch with the ooze from an active human smallpox sore. In Constantinople, certain old women were said to be especially skilled at "ingrafting" and fashionable Europeans there invited them to parties to immunize guests.

One crusader was Dr. Zabdiel Boylston of Boston (1679-1766). In 1721 he inoculated his only son, two Negro slaves, and 244 others during the aforementioned epidemic in that city. For his own pains and those of his patients, a mob stoned his house and threatened hanging. Boylston's humane effort at immunization was the first in America and resistance was fierce, particularly from the clergy who saw such acts as meddling in the ways of God.

In 1738 a Charleston, South Carolina, physician stopped a smallpox outbreak with inoculation as well as an original arm-to-arm method of passing infected matter. James Kilpatrick was not stoned. Instead his methods became part of a burgeoning inoculation technology.

An English farmer named Jesty noticed that milkmaids who contracted vaccinia, or cowpox, a disease painless and harmless to humans, seemed immune to smallpox. In 1774, scratching himself and his family and rubbing in oozings from the pustules of an infected cow, he performed the first vaccination, and successfully so.

The man who brought everything together was Edward Jenner (1749-1823), an English clergyman's son, fond of poetry, imaginative in science, rude to critics. Jenner may or may not have known of Jesty. He did know that farmers and milkmaids in his Gloucestershire practice claimed they never "took smallpox" if they once had the mild cowpox. He knew too of inoculation with human infective matter and wished it could be rendered more dependable for the patient and less lethal to those about him.

Jenner vaccinated his first patient in 1796. By 1798 he had vaccinated 22 more. He described them all in his his milestone immunization treatise *"An Inquiry into the Causes and Effects of the Variolae Vaccinae,"* printed in 1798 with four-color plates.

The literature detailing Jenner's two-year experiment is vast, and his accomplishment cannot be overvalued. He ended doubt for patient and deadliness for others which were inherent in inoculation. Using a scientific approach he hammered vague country intuitions into a sound, workable principle which has never been shaken. With vaccination, no one need ever suffer smallpox again. There need never be another century in which 60,-000,000 died. Many had imagined this. Jenner made it so.

This truth was opposed by some (professional inoculators, doctors, religious purists), but was self-evident to many.

American Indians were understandably quick to see its value. In 1812, one tribe sent him a belt and wampum, "In token of our acceptance of your precious gift, and we beseech the great spirit to take care of you in this world and in the land of spirits."

Another who appreciated it was Napoleon of France; smallpox was more a leveler of armies than were cannon or cavalry. In 1805 he ordered vaccination for all French soldiers. He too personally gave thanks in his own way.

Jenner once wrote to him asking release of an English prisoner. Napoleon said, "Ah, Jenner! I can refuse nothing to Jenner."

The vaccination doctor. An early mass immunization in a home, by a 19th century French artist.

World Health Organization

Bavaria made vaccination compulsory in 1807. Great Britain opposed it at first but affirmed in 1853. Rumania vaccinated in 1874, Austria in 1886.

Not all nations moved so wisely, however. (There is still no universal compulsory vaccination in the U.S.) Smallpox remained a prevalent disease in most of the world until the close of the 19th century.

In India (1873) a half million died. In France during the Franco-Prussian war, smallpox sickened 200,000; some 25,000 men died. French Army vaccination was limply administered. In Montreal, in 1885, a rail worker's illness was not correctly diagnosed as smallpox and 20,000 cases grew from his own. More than 3,000 died.

After 1900 this virulent smallpox form (variola major, see Definition at end of chapter) faded and a milder form (variola minor) gradually emerged. In the current century both seem to be retreating; figures of the first few decades bear out this contention.

In 1921 there were 89,357 cases and 481 deaths in the U.S. In 1945 there were 346 cases and 12 deaths. In 1950 there were 42 cases, no deaths.

The U.S. experienced its most recent smallpox scare in 1965, when a Washington, D.C. woman reported quite calmly to a clinic that she believed she had smallpox. Teams from the U.S. Public Health Service Communicable Disease Center in Atlanta, Georgia, tracked more than 1,000 who had been in contact with her during the contagious time, vaccinated them, then checked their vaccination scars and temperatures nightly for two weeks, watching for infection. One was a clinic doctor who had treated the woman; he was found on his honeymoon in a New England town. There was no smallpox flareup. The woman, as it turned out, did not have smallpox.

The last U.S. scare before the above, a bona fide case, occurred in 1949.

As the 1960's opened, the earth's smallpox reservoirs had dried to such small size many medical men regarded the disease as they do dinosaurs: extinct. Annual case report: about 70,000. A WHO Expert Committee on Smallpox stated in 1964, "The global eradication of smallpox is well within the bounds of possibility."

The program was begun in January 1967 on a $2,500,000 budget for the first year. By the end of 1968, Dr. Henderson stated, every country would be participating. Of all the international eradication programs projected, smallpox is the most promising. Dr. Henderson estimated all of South American, containing several endemic pockets would be smallpox free in five years, the entire earth in ten.

"Smallpox is the most eradicable of all diseases, one reason being, you don't have to vaccinate everyone, just large enough masses of people to interrupt transmission," he said. "If we can't eradicate this one, we can't eradicate anything."

Shortly after he said this, smallpox displayed the capricious nature common to all epidemic diseases. The first *WHO Smallpox Eradication Surveillance Report*, dated September 1967, stated:

> A total of 60,941 cases have been reported during the first 28 weeks of 1967, an increase of 40 per cent over the comparable period in 1966. The number of cases thus far reported exceeds the total of cases recorded for all of 1964 or 1965.

What effect did this unwanted bonus have on the eradication program, not yet a year old? It was too early to tell. Henderson felt the original ten-year goal was till "quite attainable." He said, "A redeployment of existing resources and tighter supervision could do the job. Of course we needed the increase like, well, like a case of smallpox."

※　　※　　※

This additional burden to the eradication program is less vexing than the opposition to it. As people mistrusted Dr. Boylston in Boston the people of endemic areas today are often indifferent to or afraid of vaccination. The field teams have only their wits and persuasiveness to overcome reluctance.

Example: In 1962 on the island of Jamaica, an immunization group drew hundreds by staging a lottery. Everyone who came received a number which was put in a drum for drawing. Those who stayed away were ineligible. Area merchants donated the prizes.

Example: South American field workers overcame reluctance in one backwater with an ingenious system of rewards for taking vaccination. For lancets they used common sewing needles and gave everyone these own needle when finished.

"This is the carnival pitchman approach, and idealists in public health object to it," Dr. Henderson says. "They call it bribery and undignified and say individuals should be educated

to come for vaccination because it is good for them. No. Get
people vaccinated now, in any way you have to. Worry about
teaching later. If you don't, by the time you set up your in-
struction program, you may just find them too sick with smallpox to teach them anything at all."

PROFILE OF SMALLPOX:

Definition: An acute, violent, painful, infectious, disfiguring
virus disease. It is the most fatal, yet most easily controlled of
all communicable diseases. Smallpox is also called variola.
There are two main forms:

1—Variola major, the most common, and most severe.
2—Variola minor (in some countries called "alastrim" or
"amaa") a milder form.

There is a third but rare fulminating form called hemorr-
haging smallpox. When it appears it is most severe at all, and
most rapid in its course to death.

Symptoms: (Almost identical for both major and minor variola.) Vomiting. Back pains. Early high fevers to 104°F. Prostration. Abdominal pains. Then the classic pimple to blister to
pustule to scab to scar pattern occurs with approximately this
timing:

Pimples appear one to five days after fever and vomiting,
etc. start.

They blister one to four days after appearance.

One to four days after blistering they form pus.

Two to six days after forming pus they form bad-smelling
scabs.

Ten to 40 days after formation, the scabs fall off, leaving
pink scars which eventually whiten.

Important Note: The above pimple to scar chain is a sure
daignostic indicator. Any disease following the pattern within
the above time limits almost must be smallpox. Another key to
identification is the spread of the pimples, etc. Eruptions,
whether scant or abundant, are symmetrical on the body and
in general. They are more profuse on exposed, irritated areas
than on protected areas or in body depressions (eyelids, behind
ears).

Important Note: When lesions are scant, they are sometimes
so few as to be overlooked altogether. Scarcity of the disease

today has dulled diagnostic familiarity. Light infections often slip by physicians. Entire hospitals are then jeopardized by a single, floating, unidentified case.

Important Note: The rare hemorrhagic smallpox is most difficult of all to diagnose. It may appear as an unimpressive toxic rash during the initial fever and be mistaken for scarlet fever or measles. Small flea bite size hemorrhages appear in the larger rash splotches, hence its name. Result: Hemorrhagic cases also slip by physicians. Death is often sudden and unheralded, occurring before the classic pimple-to-scar sequence begins.

. Old immunization (any vaccination more than three years old) may or may not influence attack severity and lessen disfiguring. Generally, even 20-year-old vaccinations effect some relief.

Fatality: Among the unvaccinated variola major claims up to 40 per cent, variola minor five per cent. Hemorrhagic is invariably fatal.

Complications: None of note. Vaccination sometimes but rarely induces secondary affects, encephalitis for one.

Infectious agent: The variola virus, so small its particles pass filters which capture most bacteria.

Occurrence: Potentially, everywhere. Endemic areas are in South America, sub-Sahara Africa and six Asiatic countries. Smallpox is repeatedly introduced into disease-free countries by travelers. Rapid air travel has brought need for merciless enforcement of vaccination procedures. Smallpox spreads most rapidly when humans crowd together, during winter indoors in temperate and arctic regions, for example. Last U.S. outbreak: Rio Grande Valley in 1949.

Reservoir: Man. No other natural animal storehouses.

Infection source: Breath, sputum of victims. Scabs, pus, other contaminated materials from skin lesions. Separated scabs remain infectious for years. Articles worn or handled by victims. Victims' clothes.

Transmission: Person-to-person, presumably by air-borne route. Contact need not be intimate. Virus travels on coughs, exhalations of victims. It may be contracted from handling a smallpox corpse. It is conveyed by clothing, books, bedclothes, etc. The virus may be carried by a third person, himself immune, from a sick person to a well one. Some epidemiologists wonder if smallpox is not the most communicable of all diseases.

Portal of infection: Mouth and/or nose, and also skin.

Incubation: Seven to 16 days from exposure to onset, nine to 12 days being average, and three to four days more to arrival of rashes.

Communicability period: From first symptoms to the time all scabs disappear, or, generally, two to three weeks. Pox is most communicable shortly before and during rash stage.

Susceptibility: Universal.

Resistance: Infection produces permanent immunity, if patient recovers. Second attacks are extremely rare. Immunization with fully potent vaccine affords temporary immunity. Three years is considered maximum safety limit before revaccination. Pregnant women should not be vaccinated unless exposed definitely to smallpox.

Specific treatment: None of any proven value. Sulfonamides or antibiotics sometimes reduce pustular stage infection, thus rendering the disease milder.

Prevention: Immunize before exposure as follows:

1—In countries where risk is slight, vaccinate all infants between five and 18 months. General vaccination of children is proven method of freeing nations from smallpox for long periods.

2—Where pox is endemic, vaccinate all children before three months old.

3—Anyone apt to contact smallpox any time; travelers, military personnel, hospital people, morticians.

Note: Previous immunity may cause light or no reaction to vaccine. Light reaction is no proof immunity persists. In doubt, revaccinate. When no reaction occurs, always revaccinate.

Control:

1—Report every case as required by International Sanitary Regulations.

2—Isolate patients, under hospital conditions and in screened quarters, until all scabs vanish.

Caution: Infection can be carried from sick room by medical personnel and visitors, and on bed linen or dust.

3—Vaccinate or revaccinate all contacts, casual or intimate. Persons even living or working where smallpox case develops are considered intimate contacts.

4—Quarantine contacts (generally for 16 days from date of exposure) if not vaccinated or revaccinated for any reason. If contacts are vaccinated or immune as a result of prior smallpox attack, merely keep under surveillance. At any temperature rise, assume smallpox and isolate. *Note:* For suspected contacts reluctant to accept surveillance, strict, arbitrary quarantine is recommended.

5—Sterilize all patients articles by steaming or boiling. Sterilize bedding. Terminal-clean sick room with formaldehyde. Burn all of patient's oral and nasal discharges.

6—Track down all contacts and sources of infection. Finding the "immediately prior case" is vital.

Basic public health measures during epidemics:

1—Search for all cases and contacts and employ necessary vaccination, quarantine, isolation or surveillance measures as described in Control above.

2—Publicize the situation objectively and stress and stress again the need for vaccination and control.

3—Provide potent vaccine to physicians and hospitals. Establish mass vaccination clinics as needed.

4—Vaccinate entire communities only when contact tracing and control methods can no longer contain infection spread.

International measures: Notify WHO and neighboring countries of first imported, transferred, or nonimported case in any area previously smallpox free. Vigorously enforce International Sanitary Regulations applying to ships, aircraft, and land transport. Each country must keep infectees and suspects inside its borders, and keep others out. Many countries require vaccination proof from all entrants, citizens and noncitizens alike, i.e. International Certificate of Vaccination. Validity of such certificates extends three years, beginning eight days after a successful vaccination.

*   *   *

The ironic theme of smallpox history cannot be recapitulated too often:

Smallpox is the easiest communicable disease to prevent, yet, there is no treatment or cure. Control is the only wall between humanity and pandemic which would kill four in ten, and from which survivors would recover scarred at the least, and possibly blind or crippled for life.

The quack doctor. The French termed syphilis the "Naples Disease." Seventeenth century charlatans touted the "sweat barrel," in which the victim sat on live coals, as a sure cure. Illustrations of the time show they did not lack gullible customers. World Health Organization

X SYPHILIS

"One night with Venus, six months with Mercury."

Syphilis and the New World were discovered together by Christopher Columbus, (1451-1506).

One Dr. Roderic Diaz of Barcelona, Spain, wrote in 1510 of a strange disease among Columbus' sailors on their return from American in 1493. In a book, *Treaties Entitled, Fruit of All Saints Against the Disease of the Island of Espanola . . . to the Common and General Good to Those Suffering from the Disease in Question, Commonly Called Bubas,* he described how:

> . . . a disease previously unknown, unseen and un-
> described first appeared in that city . . . and spread
> thence throughout the world.

The new disease was syphilis, carried from the West Indies by men aboard *Nina, Pinta,* and *Santa Maria.* Diaz was probably the first European doctor to encounter the disease, the first at any rate to note its unfamiliarity and describe its symptoms. He treated syphilis in several sailors of Columbus, among them the pilot, Pinzon of Palos.

Dr. Diaz' *Treaties* is the first recognizable account of the disease as it is known today. There is none earlier in any other language. Columbus' men were the first known to complain of it. Many early references to venereal disease, such as the "issue" frequently mentioned in the Mosaic books, probably pertain to gonorrhea or soft chancre. Ancient skeletons in China, Egypt, and Europe show no evidence of syphilitic corrosion. Ancient Greek and Roman writers, living in a time of ambitious sexual output, made no mention of the disfiguring effects of syphilis. Medieval physicians were sharp observers of human condition and they recorded no disease as violently dramatic as syphilis, so far as is known.

There is no doubt that syphilis plagued the residents of pre-Columbian Central America, however. Skeletons dating to 1000 B.C. bear classic syphilitic bone lesions. A large body of

151

evidence gives America nearly clear title as source of the disease.

There are those who disagree. They maintain evidence equally as creditable proves syphilis did occur early in Europe. The origin-of-syphilis debate is old, and several fairly respectable notions support the Europe side of the argument:

One, that the extensive human rotting and disfigurement blamed on leprosy was really caused by syphilis. Leprosy was considered highly contagious in pre-Columbian Europe, was sometimes said to be transmitted by sexual contact, had hereditary features, and responded to mercury treatment. These are characteristics of syphilis; it is possible the disease identified as leprosy was perhaps syphilis.

Two, that syphilis was "resting" for centuries as epidemic diseases mysteriously do and coincidentally burst into activity again at the time of Columbus' homecoming.

Three, that Columbus' crewmen imported a new and virulent strain of the old disease and it was not recognized as such.

Other indications are cited:

Disfiguring genital afflictions described by fifth century writers were traced to promiscuity and might well be syphilis. In the 13th century, Italy's ablest surgeon, Guglielmo Salicetti, called Saliceto (circa 1210-1277), a thorough man trained in war and university, described "cold and hot humors which proceed from the liver and cause a bubo in the groin after lying with an unclean woman." This could be syphilis; buboes are a primary stage manifestation. Saliceto's pupil, Lanfranchi of Milan (?—1315), whose support of his master contributed later to his expulsion from the city, describes chancres of the penis after lying with foul women. Chancres are another primary stage symptom.

A 1398 manuscript details a disease appearing when "a child is fed with corrupt milk of a leprous nurse." The ailment stopped the nose, altered the voice, caused hair to fall, and could have been congenital syphilis.

In July of 1463 a prostitute testified in court in Dijon, France, that she drove off an unwelcome customer, by claiming she was sick with *la grande verole*. This is one of the labels later applied to syphilis.

So the controversy goes. Whatever the outcome, for historical discussion it can be said that Columbus discovered syphilis and the New World together. The first reliable and unambiguous accounts of syphilis, or great pox as it became known, begin with his return to Spain in spring, 1493.

Syphilis is one of a group called "venereal" because they are most commonly contracted in sexual intercourse; the word venereal is derived from Venus, goddess of love. The company includes at least four others: gonorrhea, chancroid, lymphogranuloma and granuloma inguinale. The five are not grouped because they share the same causative agent but because of their sexual mode of transmission. The five diseases in fact are caused by five different agents; spirochetes, cocci, bacilli, viruses, and an entity possibly a bacterium now known as the Donovan body.

Syphilis has been epidemic for five centuries, fading at times, blasting at others, but unbroken since its first appearance in Europe.

As it came in by boat, it moved out across Europe with a marching army, the travelling companion of most communicable diseases.

In 1495, some 6,000 mercenary French troops fought several seesaw battles with a Spanish army of King Ferdinand V (1452-1516) for possession of Naples. During the shifting fighting, it happened that men of both sides slept with the same women. As it also happened, there were men among the Spanish host recently returned from the West Indies where they had contracted the disease of Columbus' sailors. When the French mercenaries eventually quit and fled to their own countries, they took the disease with them, in effect a last shot in the back from a victorious enemy. And wherever these fleeing mercenaries passed, they left syphilis behind. Syphilis at this time was not called syphilis; it had no name. The French called it the "Neopolitan disease" in bitter memory of the women of their lost battleground. Others called it the "French disease" in bitter memory of those soldiers who brought it to them.

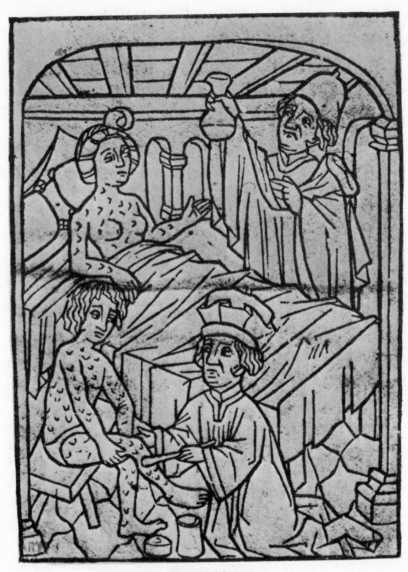

Sixteenth century therapy. Two physicians examine the spotted victims, probably man and wife, in this old woodcut. The standing doctor studies the woman's urine. The other daubs medication on the man's sores; a standard remedy was an ointment of mercury, verdigris, silver nitrate, in a base of pig and dog fat.

The disease was generally named this way at first, that is, by the source from whence it came. The Spaniards called it the Espanola disease, Espanola then being the name given Haiti. The Russians called it the Polish disease. The Indians blamed the Portuguese. The Turks and English made the French the scapegoat again.

For some reason France was most often blamed, and most of Europe soon settled for the "French disease."

The new scourge tortured millions in France, Germany, Switzerland, Holland, and Greece in 1496. The Scots were afflicted in 1497, Hungarians and Russians in 1499. Vasco de Gama's sailors infected Indian women in 1498. Other Europeans carried it in their sores to China and Japan. Jews and Mohemmedans fleeing the Spanish inquisition brought syphilis to Africa. No other disease in history has been spread so far so fast by so many. Unlike smallpox which ran its course quickly before a sufferer finished his journey, syphilis incubates for months (See Symptoms, profile at end of chapter) and as a result travels easily.

As the pestilence spread so did misconceptions concerning it. Late 15th century people believed syphilis was the same as yaws, another West Indian curse than unfamiliar to Europe. Then there evolved belief that syphilis and gonorrhea were but different faces of a common ravager.

Among the supposed causes:

Wearing linen shirts. An infected person whispering in one's ear. Marrying a leper. Divine anger. Witches' curses. Copulating with animals (also said to breed monsters half human, half whatever animal was involved).

Francis Bacon (1561-1626) reported that dishonest merchants sold French troops barrels of pickled human flesh for tuna during the Naples war. This "abominable and heavy food" caused syphilis, he wrote.

In the same war, Spanish soldiers leaving an Italian town were said to have laced tons of wine with the blood of lepers to poison invading Frenchmen. Those french soldiers who drank were riddled by overflowing sores, according to a physician to Pope Clement VII (1478-1534).

Three hundred and fifty years passed before the disease was cured of the nonsense infecting it.

The disease was so new, many physicians refused to treat it because there was nothing in Galenical therapy or pharmacopoeia prescribing for it. Galen the Physician (131-201) was a veritable production line of medical thought and innovation, and has been called the greatest Greek physician after Hippocrates. Though often fanciful and incorrect, he was the most important in western medicine and thus influenced it for 14 centuries. Galen was silent on syphilis. Galenical physicians therefore could not treat it. The silence, incidentally, it taken as another indication that there was no early *grande verole* in Europe.

Not all physicians were Galen-oriented, however. Cures, some workable, some not, were offered. One of the not workable was sasparilla, the soft drink. Hawkers ladled it from carts to sore-covered victims crowding and knocking cups together in Broad Sanctuary, London, near Westminster Abbey. Bleeding, the near homicidal remedy for just about everything, was recommended.

Among the workable was mercury. Also, Arabic ointments (*ungentum Saracenium*) were especially favored by syphilis doctors. The mercurial ointments were new new. They were used in the 12th century to medicate an indefinable group of skin eruptions known to include venereal chancroids. Those who argue the case of early syphilis in Europe claim pre-Columbian treatment means pre-Columbian disease.

In 1510 Girolamo Fracastoro the Veronese detailed the hideous assault of *la grande verole* in a poem representing a shepherd named Syphilis as the first man to suffer the disease. Fracastoro gave it the name it bears today. From his *Syphilis Sive Morbus Gallicus:*

> Soon is the body ulcerous and vile.
> The face becomes, within a little while,
> A mask of running pustules, small and great
> A horny shell that glands will irritate
> Breaking, and emptying an acrid humor
> From pus-corroded skin pours every tumor.
> And bloody ulcers deeply dig away
> Gnawing the tissues that they make their prey.
> Then man is stripped until his piteous moans
> Come from a skeleton of putrid bones.

Possibly some of syphilis' violence has been bred out over centuries. It no longer chops and ruins in its early stages quite as Fracastoro says. It possibly wrought changes dreadful to behold five centuries ago, however, for people abandoned syphilitics in the street and even lepers fled from them.

The French, blamed generously for originating the disease, were themselves generous in handling syphilitics. The Paris parliament in 1497 ordered all syphilitics from the city and decreed those who disobeyed would be "thrown into the river in case they are ever hereafter found. . . ."

The Scots of Aberdeen also in 1497 ordered that:

> For protection from the disease which has come out of France and strange parts, all light women desist from their vice and sin of venery . . . on pain, else, of being branded with a hot iron on their cheek. . . .

A chalf with six eyes, three mouths, and three noses was reported in Massachusetts Bay Colony in 1626. Birth of such monsters was superstitiously regarded as herald of some awful, divinely wrought catastrophe to come. John Winthrop, first governor of the colony (1588-1649), wrote: "What these prodigies portend the Lord only knows, and in his due time will manifest." Seldom are prophecies borne out, but Winthrop's was in great measure. The following year syphilis broke out in Massachusetts Bay, the first in New England.

In 17th century Europe there was no personal stigma implicit in syphilis. Gentlemen who had not experienced great pox at least once were considered ungentlemanly, and perhaps not manly at all.

Francis I of France (1494-1547) sprouted the telltale chancres one day and his mother said her son was being punished where he sinned.

Ivan IV of Russia (1530-1584) suffered tertiary stage cerebral syphilis (see Symptoms at chapter end) which rendered him capricious vicious and brought him his reputation as Ivan the Terrible.

The heavy metals (mercury, antimony, others) became the prime remedies. Patients were coated with mercuric ointment, filled with mercuric salts, and suffered as much from treatment as from disease. To be effective, mercury therapy had to enter a "fluxing" stage. In this stage a patient salivated constantly, lost his hair and teeth, felt knifing abdominal pains and grew foul sores in his mouth. These tortures were not short lived; treatments sometimes continued for months. "For one night with Venus," a saying went, "spend six months with Mercury."

Rest cure. Afflicted women frequently remained indoors to deal with the disease, staying until their sores sloughed off scabs and disappeared.

N.Y. Public Library

Syphilis touched countless millions of lives in its first 350 years. Though it contributed to the deaths of masses it killed few directly. Like malaria, syphilis is a chronic, slow borer. It reduces the body; death is usually caused by something else. In its hellish tertiary complications, however (See profile at chapter end), slow death by paresis and/or sudden death by syphilis-caused coronary failure are common.

In the classic but now dated *An Introduction to the History of Medicine*, fourth edition, Dr. Fielding Garrison (1870-1935) made an observation meant for an earlier time but applicable still:

> Apart from wars and famine . . . syphilis has held its own . . . as a prime factor in bring about the dengeration of the human stock.

*   *   *

The 350 years ended in mid-19th century and it is difficult to credit any one man with ending it because so many contributed so much in quick succession.

Philippe Ricord (1799-1889) determined that syphilis and gonorrhea were different things in 2,500 tests between 1831 and 1837, a most important development. Ricord was a pessimist who relished cynical anecdotes of morality. He was once called "the Voltaire of pelvic literature," by Oliver Wendell Holmes.

Chancroid and syphilis were differentiated in 1852.

In 1905 in Berlin protozoologist Fritz Schaudinn discovered syphilis' infective organism, till that time invisible, using a microscopic technique known as dark field examination. It proved a spirochete, named by Schaudinn *Treponema pallidum*. Schaudinn's promising productivity ended early, at 35, with death in 1906.

In 1906 August von Wasserman (1866-1925) and two others developed the test for detecting *Treponema pallidum* in the blood, so familiar today it is called simply "the Wasserman."

In 1909 Paul Ehrlich (1854-1915) announced discovery of salvarsan, the arsphenamine compound called the "magic bullet" because one injection theoretically kills the syphilis spirochetes so quickly, also called "606" because it was the 606th compound Ehrlich and his assistants tested.

In the 1940s the penicillin discovery of Sir Alexander Fleming (1881-1955) was used against syphilis, finally achieving in days the cures that took so much longer before, bringing treatment within price range and endurance of all patients.

These were important achievements, described often in detailed books as they deserve, but best judged by the results they produce.

Penicillin has proven to be "queen of drugs" in syphilis treatment for 25 years. Between 1950 and 1958, it halved the rate of new cases. Its side effects are few. The syphilis organism has not developed resistance as other organisms have done.

Medical research has yet to find immunization for syphilis; such will probably be the next breakthrough of importance. Dr. Thorstein Guthe, chief medical officer of WHO's venereal diseases and treponematoses unit, stated in fall 1967: "You can't 'treat' such a communicable disease out of existence with drugs. We have two dozen drugs now available to treat syphilis, where we had only one 20 years ago, and we still have syphilis. To rid ourselves of it we also need an immunizing agent."

Holding up syphilis immunization research in particular is reluctance of *Treponema pallidum* to breed in captivity. Under laboratory conditions it does not grow in quantities large enough for experimental needs. Finding out why is slow work but there are some significant results. According to Dr. Guthe:

● Research workers in Wroclaw, Poland, have kept the syphilis organism active and disease producing for 16 days *in vitro*.

● Experimenters in Los Angeles have found that *Treponema pallidum* grown in animals, then attenuated by gamma radiation, grants rabbits limited immunity.

● Danish and American research workers are close to defining the metabolic requirements of *Treponema pallidum*. This is important. Before the spirochete can be raised in bulk scientists must know what nourishment it needs.

Holding up research in general is shortage of research workers. In late 1967, according to Dr. Guthe, there were only 12 laboratories in the world committed to syphilis research to any significant degree, and, in face of a rise in syphilis in the world, the number of laboratories was shrinking.

The cost of unbridled syphilis is inevitably far greater than the bill for research into immunization. In the U.S. annual productive time lost by individuals collapsing in advanced stage syphilis-induced insanity totals more than 32,000 years. Losses due to syphilitic heart damage add up to more than 7,000 years. Loss to blindness: more than 26,000 years. Loss of income: More than $80,000,000 a year. The cost of instituionalizing the syphilitic insane tops $47,000,000 and the syphilitic blind, more than $12,000,000. (Estimates are projections of 1956 figures.)

* * *

There is epidemic syphilis loose in the world again. Following dramatic decline between 1950 and 1958 the incidence curve turned and climbed upward. Some countries are now burdened with almost the same caseloads they carried in the peak year before 1950. Some carry even more; France, in 1965, 40 per cent more. Disease rates are on the upstroke, in cities in particular, among adolescents and young adults in general. In some countries the incidence rate was higher in fall of 1967 than during the epidemics of World War Two, before penicillin was so plentiful.

A penicillin backlash is one reason. The antibiotic is now easy to procure, costs little, cures after one or a few painless treatments. These qualities have generated a side effect of indifference to both the infection and its consequences. Respect for "the syph" painfully learned during months with Mercury is now lost.

Second, Dr. Guthe finds still other reasons of sociological nature for the new epidemic: industralization, increase and/or new patterns in homosexuality and prostitution, the flow of young country people to crowded cities, breaking of old family patterns and old ways, with subsequent breaking of sexual taboos. All indicate ". . . a new dimension in morals."

Third, nations themselves are responsible for the fresh attack. *The Work of WHO, 1966,* states:

> . . . approximately half the 147 countries and areas presenting reviews . . . expressed disquietude at the significant and consistent upward trend of venereal diseases in recent years, often especially marked in the younger age groups. . . .

> Notwithstanding these trends, only a few health administrations are intensifying their efforts in planning venereal disease control programs based on epidemiological principles.

There are 30-50 millions carrying syphilis through the world today, by WHO statistics. Millions more uncounted extra-statistical cases either hide their infection out of shame or don't know they have it at all. One reason for this unwanted plenty is, as *The Work of WHO* states, inaction by nations. Another is the difficulty in reaching the people themselves. For gonnorhea, the estimate is upward of 150 millions.

Great delicacy is sometimes involved. "How do you tactfully suggest treating women for venereal disease in areas where women are held sacred and even speaking to them of venereal disease or suggesting they might need treatment for it is grave insult?" Dr. Guthe once asked.

The difficulty is sometimes insurmountable.

PROFILE OF SYPHILIS:

Definition: An acute, chronic, relapsing, highly contagious, spirochete-caused, slow evolving and sometimes crippling and disfiguring venereal disease. Origin of the word is uncertain. It is probably Greek, a combination of *syn* meaning "together" and *philein* meaning "to love" or else comes from *siphlos*, which means "crippled." There are two main distinctive forms:

1—Venereal syphilis, indicating infection by bodily contact, usually sexual in 90 to 95 per cent of its cases.

2—Endemic syphilis, or "bejel," is of nonvenereal spread, and is thus sometimes called *syphilis innocentum*. Endemic syphilis is a disease of primitive and unsanitary conditions, present in eastern Mediterranean and arid African regions. It does not occur in the United States.

Note: This profile covers only venereal syphilis, named after Venus, goddess of love. The venereal variety is by far the more prevalent than the endemic. Venereal is the most destructive, often bringing paralysis, mental deterioration, a "rotting flesh" condition of mucous membranes, and disease of heart and blood vessels in its later or tertiary stage. Synonyms are: VD, the great pox.

Symptoms: Venereal syphilis is a three-stage disease, duration calculated in years and lifetimes rather than days. Each stage exhibits characteristics serving as revealing diagnostic clues to the sharp observer. The last (tertiary) stage is ruinous to the victim's body and sanity, grotesque to observe, and its consequences irreversible.

1—Primary stage: About three weeks after intercourse primary lesions called chancres appear in the area of sexual contact, usually the genitals, and sometimes the mouth. Kissing also transmits the disease. A mouth containing syphilis chancres is a rich infection bed. Chancres are haru, small bumps which erode and ulcerate. They are generally painless and often do not alarm the victim. As the spirochetes invade the blood from their foci in the chancres, nearby lymph glands may swell, causing buboes. (*Note:* Infection without chancre is fairly common.) In four to six weeks the chancres shrink and the inside of the mouth grows raw. These conditions indicate the beginning of the . . .

2—Secondary stage: It is symptomized generally by mild overall bodily disturbances as spirochetes spread and relocate in the body. It is symptomized specifically by: Fever. Anemia. Lesions and reddish brown spots which persist a week or two. Moist patches between toes, other moist skin regions. Sometimes, but rarely, loss of hair. Muscle and joint pains.

As in primary stage, these signs are often mild, bearable, overlooked, or purposely overlooked by terrified victims. Above mentioned fevers may resemble those of malaria and be mistaken for such.

Secondary stage symptoms disappear spontaneously and untreated within a year. They may reappear occasionally, along with eye, skin, and central nervous system lesions, but always reappear gently.

Note: Venereal syphilis is communicable only in these first two stages. Infectiousness ends as it enters the . . .

3—Tertiary stage: Spirochetes move to all parts of the body, concentrate in certain favorite tissues, build up, cause vast damage. It is difficult to say when tertiary syphilis begins. Perhaps it takes five years, perhaps 20. The symptoms are simple to identify and unmistakable when they appear: vast noninfectious skin and mucosal surface eruptions which seem to literally dissolve flesh and leaving gaping holes, often at the nose and mouth. Bone lesions. Hardening of the arties due to scar tissue buildup. Destruction of brain and spinal cord. Result is creeping paralysis and mental deterioration which often reduces the sufferer to a vegetative state.

Occurrence: Venereal syphilis is one of the most widespread communicable diseases. It appears in every climate, every country. It involves the young mostly, between 15 and 30 years, because they are the most sexually active. It is prevalent among male homosexuals. Since 1957 incidence has increased throughout much of the world.

Reservoir: Man.

Infection source: Spirochete-bearing matter released by apparent or hidden (in urethra or vaginal passage) moist early lesions of infected persons. Also, body fluids such as saliva, blood, vaginal discharges, during infectious stages.

Transmission: Person to person. Loose spirochetes (See above Infection Source.) are deposited by infected person on skin or muscous membranes of an uninfected person during intercourse, generally in genital area, slightly less often the mouth. The spirochetes enter through skin breaks; even microscopic breaks are large enough. They multiply in the freshly infected person, eventually cause lesions and spill out. At this point (and during secondary stage eruptions), the spirochetes can be passed to still another to further spread the disease. Infection of venereal syphilis' severity is rarely spread by indirect contact with contaminated articles. One outside the body, *Treponema pallidum* lives only about six hours.

Endemic syphilis, mentioned above, *is* transmitted by indirect contact with contaminated objects, most often eating and drinking utensils.

Prental infection takes place after the fourth month of pregnancy.

Syphilis is occasionally passed via blood transfusion.

Portal of infection: The skin. (See Transmission above)

Incubation: Ten days to ten weeks, usually three weeks, from contact to first lesion.

Communicability period: During primary and secondary stage only, as already indicated, and during reappearances of secondary stage manifestations. *Important:* Actual time span of communicability is uncertain but is felt to be as long as four years from infection. In either stage, proper treatment usually terminates infectivity in 24 hours.

Susceptibility: Everyone is susceptible.

Resistance: There is no immunity, either natural or man-given. Infection develops only slight resistance which is easily overcome by a massive reinfection or destroyed by any treatment given during first two stages.

Specific treatment: Long-acting penicillin (PAM, benzathine penicillin). Administer large doses at diagnosis to insure some long reach medication should the patient not return. Penicillin-sensitive persons should receive erythromycin or tetrayclines.

Prevention: Measures in this section apply to *all* venereal diseases: syphilis, chancroid, lymphogranuloma venerum, granuloma inguinale, and gonorrhea.

1—Promote health and sex education, premarital and prenatal examinations.

2—Suppress commercial vice.

3—Encourage personal prophylaxis before, during, after intercourse in sex education programs.

4—Provide diagnosis and treatment facilities for all regardless of economic status. Repeat mass blood tests in all areas or groups of known high disease incidence.

5—Seek out persons past infective stage to prevent their suffering relapses and tertiary stage disabilities.

Important: In implementing steps four and five avoid embarrassing or intimidating victims who are already most likely apprehensive of public exposure and fearful of the disease itself. Respect personal dignity. Otherwise victims are not likely to appear voluntarily for treatment. They will remain infected and continue to infect others.

Control: Report every case to local health authorities. Track down all contacts. The stage of the victim's infection determines the length to which investigators must go in tracing contacts.

1—In primary syphilis, cover all sexual partners of preceding three months.

2—In secondary, all partners of preceding six months.

3—In case of tertiary, locate all partners of the preceding year if time elapsed since infective primary and secondary lesions is unknown. Also cover all sexual partners and children of infected mothers.

4—In congenital syphilis, examine all members of the patient's immediate family.

Basic public health measures during epidemics: Same as those of Prevention and Control, only wider and more intense in application.

International measures: Examine adolescent and young adult groups crossing borders from high prevalence countries. Scrupulously enforce international agreements concerning diagnosis and treatment of merchant seamen, the Brussels Agreement of 1924, for one. Nations should quickly pass along all information specified under such agreements.

". . . so fatal as often to deter the practitioner even from attempting a cure."

If the number of victims that a disease claims is the measure of its significance, then all diseases, particularly the most dreadful infectious diseases such as bubonic plague, Asiatic cholera must rank far behind tuberculosis. Statistics teach that one seventh of all human beings die of tuberculosis, and that if one considers only the productive middle age group, tuberculosis often carries away one third, and often more, of these.

—Robert Koch, discover of tubercle bacillus, in his treatise, "The Etiology of Tuberculosis," 1882

Tuberculosis is an unsparingly vicious bacillary disease of uncertain origin and such great age it was afflicting mankind in company with smallpox and a few others before written history. Skeletons of prehistoric hunchbacks show tuberculosis had twisted their spines.

TB, *phthisis*, consumption, white plague, lupus, tabes, whatever it is called, seldom travels or works alone. It prefers to add its own deaths to those of war, famine, poverty, other epidemic diseases. A full-blown tuberculosis outbreak has not been recorded since early 19th century, which gives the disease a false reputation for being easygoing. Tuberculosis still infects and kills millions yearly.

The first known tuberculosis reference appears in the Hammurabic Code, written earlier than 2000 B.C. The Greek poet Homer described ". . . a grevious consumption that separates soul and body." Fifteen centuries before Christ, Indo-Ayran priests in what is now India prayed, "Oh, Fever, with thy Brother Consumption, with thy Sister Cough, go to the people below!"

In the Bible (The Book of Deuteronomy, chapter 28, verse 22) the Israelites were warned of another of their seemingly endless punishments: "The Lord shall smite thee with a consumption and with a fear, and with an inflammation . . ." Deu-

167

teronomy is dated at 700 B.C. or thereabouts. Consumption is one of the names given tuberculosis.

Pre-Hippocratic Greeks sorely suffered something they called *phthisis*, from the verb meaning "to dry up." For its cure the Greeks prescribed fresh food, milk, and sea voyages for fresh air, all remedies still considered helpful.

Hippocrates knew *phthisis* and described lung ulcerations which seem suspiciously tubercular. Galen knew *phthisis*, too, observed "ulcers of the trachea" (possibly scrofulous abcesses on the neck or nodules in the throat). His fresh air retreat on Capri may have been the world's first clinic. Galen was one of the first to suspect communicability of tuberculosis from one person to another.

The disease entered Europe through the same doorway taken by many others; Greece. From there it spread to Rome. The Romans provided the transport to the rest of Europe. As they brought *pax Romanum,* so they brought *phthisis* everywhere they went.

For the next 12 centuries the disease flickered everywhere in the known world. It is thought to number among the forces which rid Europe of leprosy so suddenly during the Middle Ages; it killed so many thousands of leoprosy's victims.

Remedies favored during these dismal centuries were rooted in old time religion, old time medicine, and old time quackery. Except for those calling for fresh food, fresh air, and rest, the remedies were by and large useless and often beyond belief in cruelty.

- The Persian astute writer-physician Rhazes and Avicenna (980-1037) thought highly of asses' milk cure. A later English physician thought so little of it he once asked whether ". . . ass patient or ass doctor was the greater ass."

- In Spain tuberculosis patients drank human blood, and were still doing so in the 1930s. In this decade, an eight-year-old boy was seized, thrust into a sack, dumped out in the patient's room, and undressed. A quack doctor told him to stop whimpering, then shoved a knife into his left armpit. The patient drank the gushing blood as the boy died.

- The stench of cow barns, inhaled a few minutes daily was often prescribed.

- Adolphe Sax (1814-1894) Belgian inventor of the saxophone, claimed that blowing wind instruments strengthened the lungs and was valuable consumption therapy.

Though it has plagued the earth from pre-history onward, tuberculosis was a late comer as a classic, all engulfing epidemic disease. Why did it wait? Again, epidemiologists do not know.

In England pulmonary disease deaths were high in mid-17th century, slid slowly downhill afterward, then lofted to new highs in mid-19th century. European and American death records show much the same trend in the 19th century, that is, a peak about 1850, a downward slide ever since.

● In the early part of the 19th century, U.S. tuberculosis deaths topped 400 per 100,000 population annually. European deaths were 500 per 100,000.

● Thirteen of every 100 white prisoners in a Philadelphia penitentary died of tuberculosis between 1829 and 1845. Death rates among Negro prisoners was higher still.

● Autopsies showed 250 out of 696 at *Hospital de la Charite* in Paris in the early 1800s had succumbed to tuberculosis.

● In 1844, all 78 boys and 91 of 94 girls in an English workhouse were infected.

● In 1850, 17 in every 1,000 French soldiers bore running scrofulous lesions, certain sign of tubercular lymph glands.

In 1815 Thomas Young (1773-1829), one of the earliest decipherers of Egyptian hieroglyphs, physicist, optical pioneer, and perhaps the most highly educated physician of his time, said in his *Historical and Practical Treatise on Consumptive Diseases:*

> Of all hectic affections, by far the most important is pulmonary consumption, a disease so frequent as to carry off prematurely about one fourth part of the inhabitants of Europe, and so fatal as often to deter the practitioner even from attempting a cure.

✻   ✻   ✻

In 1838 and 1839 in England 30 per cent of all deaths among laborers were the result of tuberculosis,

Labor held no monopoly on misery. Alexandre Dumas pere (1802-1870) wrote: ". . . everyone was consumptive, and especially the poets. It was good form to spit blood from sheer emotion."

Henry David Thoreau (1817-1862), America's celebrated rugged individualist and civil disobedient, died of tuberculosis.

So did Robert Louis Stevenson (1850-1894).

So did the German poet Johann Schiller (1759-1805).

So did the German composer Karl Maria von Weber (1786-1826).

So did English poet John Keats (1795-1821), and violinist Nicolo Paganini (1782-1840), and composer Frederic Chopin (1810-1849), who was carried on a pig boat from Majorca just before he died spitting blood.

Their examples fired the imaginations of Romantic Era figures, and a tubercular death became a desirable thing, if one had to die at all. The English poet Lord Byron (1788-1824) once told a friend during an illness, "I look pale. I should like to die of a consumption."

"Why?" the friend asked.

"Because the ladies would say, 'Look at that poor Byron. How interesting he looks in dying.' "

Pale people became fashionable. Robust ones took to lemon juice and vinegar to kill their appetites. One French journalist said Byron's remark and his melancholy poetry caused a run on lemons at the greengrocers'. It is likely that with so much of the disease about, those men and women who depleted their bodies to achieve the stylish consumptive look eventually fell prey to consumption.

Romantic Age people imagined a link between tuberculosis and genius; in currency was a notion that tuberculosis patients possessed more drive than people free of the disease. The afflicted themselves were guilty of encouraging the notion.

Elizabeth Barrett Browning (1806-1861) described her own talent as "a butterfly within, fluttering for release."

John Addington Symonds (1840-1893), the noted scholar, claimed tuberculosis had enriched his life with a "wonderful Indian summer of experience."

The genius-through-disease notion prevailed into the 20th century, possibly because the gifted people who had the disease could afford to indulge it more than others. In a 1932 book, *Pulmonary Tuberculosis,* Arthur Fishberg (1898-   ) states:

> Tuberculosis patients, particularly young talented individuals . . . display enormous intellectual capacity of the creative kind. Especially is this to be noted in those who are of the artistic temperament, or who have a talent for imaginative writing . . . despite the fact that it hurts their physical condition, they keep on working and produce their best works.

Katherine Mansfield (1888-1923), herself tuberculous, saw this productive restlessness in her own physician. "He has the disease himself," she wrote. "I recognize the smile—just a shade too bright—and his strange joyousness as he came to meet me—the gleam—the faint flitter on the plant that the frost has laid a finger on."

It is not impossible that there may be some link between tuberculosis and bursts of insight and output. To a degree any low fever (a manifestation of tuberculosis) stimulates action and heightens perception.

Many were not so self-deceptive. They recognized the disease as a waster and had no romantic notions concerning tuberculosis-derived ambitions. John Keats was one. Arriving in Naples too burnt out to romp about the bay and steamy Mt. Vesuvius, he said, "Oh! What a misery it is to have an intellect in splints."

This romantic ideal was described by Thomas Beddoes (1760-1808) in an *Essay on the Causes, Early Signs of, and Prevention of Pulmonary Consumption,* published 1799:

> The emaciated figure strikes one with terror; the forehead covered with drops of sweat; the cheeks painted with a livid crimson, the eyes sunk; the little fat that raised them in their orbits entirely wasted; the pulse quick and tremulous; the nails long, bending over the ends of the fingers; the breath offensive, quick, and laborious, and the cough so incessant as scarce to allow the wretched sufferer time to tell his complaints.

※　　※　　※

Belief that tuberculosis is contagious is an old one, supported at times, damned at others, misapplied at still others, but persistent for centuries.

Girolamo Fracastoro the Veronese suggested tuberculosis' talent for contagion in 1545. Others set out to prove the master clinician was correct often with more fancy than fact. An Italian physician reported seeing men fall dead after merely stepping on the sputum of tuberculosis victims. Another maintained individuals contracted the ailment by inhaling fumes of spittle bubbling on burning coals. In 1697 a German doctor reportedly became tuberculous after tasting his patients' sputum to diagnose their illness. Italian anatomists in the 18th century refused to dissect corpses of tuberculous victims; they feared any contact, even a post mortem one.

In 1699 in Italy the first antituberculosis legislation was passed. Ferdinand VI of Spain (1713-1759) was impressed and wrote strict laws for his own country. A punishment for disobedience was a fine of 300 ducats and three years in chains, pulling oars in the prison galleys. Spanish law barring consumptives from the New World is said to have kept Spanish colonies tuberculosis free while the disease was everywhere in the French and English holdings.

There was spasms of dissent against the contagion theory, however.

Some were honest. The university faculties came to feel the disease was hereditary. Reason: in certain families many members became consumptive, in other families no one did, all circumstances indicating contagion rather than consanguinity.

Some were venal. Strict enforcement proved costly to governments sometimes, and harmful to trade.

The dissenters were effective and by mid-18th century most of the earlier strictness was legislated away. A new Neopolitan tuberculosis law in 1754 paid only slight service to the contagion theory, leaving it to the individual doctor to "educate his phthisical patients to the wisdom of precautionary measures."

During these centuries many figures battled and/or shaped these trends of thought.

René Théophile Hyacinthe Laennec performed nearly 400 autopsies and in March 1804 stated that many unassociated lung ailments and their stages and clinical symptoms were all forms of the one disease. It was named tuberculosis in 1839 by a Swiss physician because the tubercle (the small round nodule produced by *Mycobacterium tuberculosis*) is the characteristic lesion of the disease (see following profile).

Laennec also designed, built, then improved upon the first practical tool for diagnosis of tuberculosis and other diseases in 1819. He called it a stethoscope, combining two Greek words, *stethos* or chest, and *skopein*, to examine. The first stethoscope was a paper cone inspired by the children's game of sending "messages" by pin scratch along wooden beams, and was used to sound the heart beat of a woman patient. Laennec detailed stethoscopic diagnosis in *Traité de l'Auscultation Médiate*. The book is the base of modern auscultation, defined as "the act of listening for sounds within the body, chiefly for ascertaining the condition of the lungs, heart, pleura, abdomen, and other organs. . . ."

These masterful breakthroughs brought Laennec the title "greatest of teachers on pulmonary tuberculosis," installing him among that vast number of men whom medicine has named "father of . . ." or "greatest of . . ." one specialty or another.

In August 1826, Laennec died of tuberculosis at age 45, after first removing the rings from his own fingers rather than burden others with the unpleasant chore.

In 1882 Robert Koch the bearded German bacteriologist ferreted out the disease organism, *Mycobacterium tuberculosis*, after 270 attempts under stress and in isolation at Charity Hospital in Berlin. Koch's discovery was a major research achievement of the 19th century, backed up by an enormous body of evidence. Its importance was not its originality (much of Koch's information and many of his methods were familiar) but its vast blessed meaning to mankind.

Koch (also discoverer of anthrax and cholera organisms) ended the contagion-hereditary debate; communicability has not been questioned since. He identified the creature which communicates it. Last, by identifying it, he rendered it vulnerable to assault and defeat.

There followed drugs, treatments and techniques to which tuberculosis is more or less vulnerable. Koch himself in 1890 announced discovery of a substance, tuberculin (manufactured from tubercle bacilli) which supposedly killed patients instead of curing them. Tuberculin was later proven useful as a detector and is still the substance used for determining susceptibility to tuberculosis. Koch received the Nobel Prize in 1905.

Roentgen Rays, or X-Rays, discovered by Wilhelm Roentgen (1845-1922) in Germany in 1895, made it possible to see the tuberculosis cavities and lesions heard by means of Laennec's stethoscope.

The American physician Edward Trudeau (1848-1915), himself riddled with tuberculosis, established the U.S. sanitorium system at Lake Saranac, New York, following the same fresh food, fresh air, and rest direction Galen employed to manage and control tuberculosis cases.

In 1924 Léon Calmette and Camille Guérin tested a workable vaccine in trials involving 664 Paris school children. The vaccine was given their names (Bacillus Calmette-Guérin), and better known as BCG, is still favored.

Stretpomycin was discovered in 1944. Other antibiotics appeared soon after. (See Specific Treatment, profile at end of chapter.) Recently, in December 1967, Lederle Laboratories, a U.S. pharmaceutical firm made available ethambutol, a compound to be used in alliance with these other older remedies. Rounding out the therapeutic picture is surgical collapse and surgical section of the lung (removal of all or part) to give invalid patients the power to walk again with reasonable assurance against relapse.

These riches of research have put an end to the nonsense of tuberculosis. In 1851, for example, the *London National and Military Gazette* recommended such worthy tuberculosis preventatives as wearing moustaches in winter to filter cold air entering the lungs. No more.

Research to date has not fully controlled tuberculosis anywhere, however. Nor has it come even close to eradication as the international health organizations envision it.

Tuberculosis still plagues the earth.

*   *   *

This is the present state of tuberculosis:

At least 15,000,000 suffer infectious tuberculosis today in the world and 3,000,000 die of it annually; these are conservative WHO estimates. *World Health Organization*

True, the mortality rate has bottomed in the economically developed countries. Between 1950 and 1960 tuberculosis deaths plummeted from 15 to two per 100,000 in the Netherlands, from 21 to 6 in the United States, and from 122 to 31 in Japan. The number of sufferers has not declined nearly as fast as the number of deaths, however, and tuberculosis still remains a curse even in the wealthy countries. Two to three million new cases appear world wide annually.

Surveys of the world's underdeveloped areas show one in every 100 may be infected. Even more serious, 70 per cent of the children may be stricken before age 14. In India alone there may be 3,000,000 infectees. In Latin America there are 600,000 known active cases and supposedly 2,000,000 undeclared ones.

A WHO Expert Committee on Tuberculosis in 1963 created a yardstick by which any country can measure its progress in eliminating tuberculosis:

When the number of children who become infected before age 14 drops below one per cent, the disease can be considered eliminated.

Not a single country in the world today had reached this mark as of fall 1967.

The U.S. Public Health Service, then starting up an isoniazid prophylaxis program for tuberculin positive persons said it hoped to reach the eradication point in 15 years.

The fugitive in any control or eradication program is one referred to as the ''Breakdown Man'' by Dr. Halfdan Mahler, chief medical officer of the WHO tuberculosis unit. "Everyone who has ever been infected is a potential 'breakdown man,' " Mahler said in fall 1967. "Once a man has had tuberculosis he always carries tuberculosis in his body, whether his disease was arrested or cured. He is, then, a potential risk wherever he goes. There are no currently available tests that will tell us definitely yes, this person will break down exactly at such and such a time, or no, he will never break down at all."

According to Shirley Ferebee, research division chief of the U.S. Public Health Service, as of fall 1967 there were 25,000,-000 in the U.S. carrying tubercle bacilli in one stage or another.

*　　*　　*

All tuberculosis control programs have the same two basic parts: (1) BCG vaccination of children, good for at least ten years. (2) Drug therapy for those persons already infected, which Dr. Mahler estimates at $10 cost per person per year. The vaccination is sometimes too technical and the cost too great for underdeveloped countries to handle. Every so often, however, there appears an opportunistic individual who makes the programs work despite such difficulties.

One day recently a trainee in a WHO-assisted laboratory technician course in Mysore, India, was watching a film at a local theatre. He heard several in the audience coughing violently.

During intermission he went to his dispensary, returned with sputum collection cups and gathered specimens from the coughers. The following morning he microscoped them; two specimens contained tubercle bacilli.

The trainee received an unlimited free pass to all new films for as long as he remained in the village.

PROFILE OF TUBERCULOSIS:

Definition: A chronic, wasting, highly infectious, but long developing bacterial disease which is a fearsome, major cause of death in many parts of the world. Its principal form is pulmonary tuberculosis which devastates the lungs. Nonpulmonary, or extrapulmonary tuberculosis cases are rare, numbering one case in ten or less. Nonpulmonary chiefly affects lymph nodes, joints, kidneys, intestines, larynx, skin, genitals. Children are most susceptible to both kinds.

Tuberculosis breaks down into specialized types as all communicable diseases do. There are 41 (See *Dorland's Illustrated Medical Dictionary*, 24th edition) affecting animals and fowl as well as man. Synonyms: TB, galloping consumption, great white plague.

Symptoms: Pulmonary tuberculosis runs a varying course, symptoms peaking and subsiding throughout, and is capable of arrest then explosive recurrence at any point during its three stages (minimal, advanced, far advanced). It is slow in onset and may be in a moderately advanced stage before symptoms show themselves, the gentler ones in the minimal stage, the harsher ones appearing as the disease progresses. In early stages tuberculosis is often mistaken for mild, chronic bronchitis.

Outward symptoms in general order of appearance, from gentle to harsh: cough, fatigue, weight loss, "night sweats." Violent coughing with hemorrhage and spitting blood, pleurisy. Infective organisms in sputum.

Principal tuberculosis site is the lung. A typical tubercular lung in advanced state (as seen by roentgenogram) is characterized by cavities left by erupting infection pockets, and scars of healed cavities, in upper parts of the lung. Immediately below there are smaller cavities. In the lower regions appear shot-sized tubercles, the characteristic lesions from which the disease spreads.

Briefly, ulceration and eruption of above-mentioned pockets is the trigger of the complicated chain of events leading to tuberculosis spread. Eruption pours semiliquid material containing infectious organisms into the bronchial tree where they meet and form new tuberculosis infection.

Diagnosis is confirmed by appearance of infective organisms in sputum, saliva, or throat swabbings, by X-Ray, by tuberculin test.

Fatality: Tuberculosis is the chief cause of death in much of the world. More than 15,000,000 are stricken annually; of these,

3,000,000 die. World mortality rates range from five to 100 deaths per 100,000. In the United States mortality is higher among males than females, higher in cities than in rural areas.

Complications: Often miliary tuberculosis, a generalized body infection occurring when infection is discharged into blood stream through a bursting tuberculous pocket in a vein wall. The scattering of infective nodules throughout the body has been likened to a scattering of millet seeds hence the name "miliary." This is a grave development striking the body everywhere. It can progress from either pulmonary or nonpulmonary type. Meningitis is another frequent complication. Also, any one of several simultaneous conditions can develop during deterioration of bodily defenses, empyema, for one.

Infection agent: *Mycobacterium tuberculosis,* a rodshaped bacillus between three and four microns long, of the same genus of organism as *Mycobacterium leprae,* the supposed cause of leprosy. Human type *Mycobacterium tuberculosis* causes nearly all pulmonary tuberculosis. A bovine variety of *Mycobacterium tuberculosis* causes most extrapulmonary cases.

Occurrence: Worldwide distribution, most prevalent in densely populated areas where poverty prevails. U.S. in 1964 recorded 50,000 new cases, 8,303 of which died.

Reservoir: Primarily man. Also tuberculosis-infected cattle.

Infection source: Breath or sputum of persons with "open" or bacillus-positive pulmonary tuberculosis. Droplets blown out by a cough or sneeze may float for hours, contain hundreds of tubercle bacili. Principal source of infection by way of alimentary tract is milk from tuberculous cattle.

Transmission: Principal routes are those indicated under Infection Source, that is, air-borne or in milk. Indirect contact with contaminated articles is not a major transmission route as was once feared. Nonpulmonary tuberculosis is not directly communicable.

Portal of infection: Lungs and alimentary tract, as cited above.

Incubation: From infection to first visible primary lung lesions, four to six weeks. Time from infection to progressive pulmonary or extrapulmonary manifestation may span years.

Communicability period: This lasts as long as a patient discharges infective organisms, perhaps for years.

Susceptibility: Everyone is prey. Most susceptible are children under age three. People suffering fatigue, malnutrition, silicosis, or diabetes are particularly vulnerable.

Resistance: Healed primary infection produces limited immunity of doubtful value and undetermined degree. Vaccination

of uninfected (tuberculin negative) persons with Bacillus Calmette Guérin (BCG) bestows definite, though partial immunity.
BCG is a vaccine specifically for infants consisting of living
cultures of bovine tubercle bacilli of greatly reduced virulence.

Specific treatment: Active pulmonary tuberculosis requires: Hospitalization. Antimicrobial drugs, namely, isoniazid (INH), para-
aminosalicylic acid (PAS), streptomycin (SM), for at least a
year. Removal of all or part of lung, other thoracic surgery.
Important: As periodic sputum tests indicate resistance to drugs,
change in antimicrobial agents is probably necessary. Drug
therapy generally converts sputum from positive to negative in
six months.

Extrapulmonary tuberculosis requires antimicrobial therapy as
well as pulmonary does, and often surgery, depending upon
tissues affected and extent of the disease.

Prevention: Tuberculosis boasts an exhaustive list of preventive measures. Important ones are:

1—Public health education.

2—X-Ray and laboratory examinations for patients, family
and household contacts, and suspects. Hospitalization and drugs
for patients.

3—BCG vaccination of uninfected persons, infants particularly,
in high mortality areas.

4—Public health nursing for home patients.

5—Tuberculosis tests for cattle, slaughter of those infected.

6—Routine X-Rays and/or tuberculin tests for groups dis-
playing high tuberculosis rates.

7—Chemoprophylaxis for: Contacts of active cases. Groups
or populations facing extraordinary infection risk. Arrested
cases never before treated with drugs. Persons showing change
from tuberculin negative to tuberculin positive in tests.

Control: Report all cases to local health authorities; reports
are obligatory in most countries. Start hospital treatment, testing, nursing, vaccination as indicated generally under Prevention, above. Isolate open tuberculosis patients who ignore basic
sanitary precautions (covering mouth when sneezing, for one).
Note: Quarantine is unnecessary.

Basic public health measures during epidemics: In addition to
measures above, broaden reconnaissance for new cases. Scour
epidemic area to find infective sources of new cases.

International measures: None.

XII THE ONLY HOPE

"I am not in WHO because the work is easy.
I am in WHO because it is worthwhile. . . ."

In the early 1960s the same complaint was heard again and again from public health field teams:

Blood samples sent for testing arrived at laboratories unfit for use. They were sometimes too old, having been in transit for long periods. Heat affected them. Moisture contaminated them. Glass tubes arrived broken. Shipping costs were high. Equipment was bulky. Local trainees were sometimes unfamiliar with its use. And so on.

Problem: Develop a simple, efficient, inexpensive method for shipping samples for testing.

The WHO supply service, often called upon to hurdle technological problems and administrative morasses in filling needs of WHO member countries, considered this blood sampling problem.

Blotting paper was eventually suggested, along with this method for its use: Soak up blood sample with small blotters which can bear the owners' identification. Allow the blood to dry. Send the blotters to the laboratories by ordinary mail, many in the same envelope. Reconstitute the samples with proper solutions in the laboratories.

This answer then offered another problem. There were no blotting papers on medical supply shelves anywhere in useable size and quality.

WHO's supply service shopped about and found: (1) A French firm able to supply sterile, high quality paper, and (2) a Swiss bookbinder willing to cut the French paper into discs about the size of a U.S. ten-cent piece. The bookbinder guaranteed uniform size and precision edges, both of which were important to WHO for packaging reasons.

Today field teams carry white, moistureproof, bacteriaproof plastic tubes, each containing 100 discs. A dozen tubes fit in a man's pocket; they contain enough discs to sample 1,200 people. The glass tubes, corks, cases, and shipping containers necessary for blood sampling of 1,200 in the conventional way require a small truck.

WHO supply service reports that any mistrust of the discs usually vanishes the first time a technician finds he can drop an entire day's work into one envelope at the nearest postoffice.

*   *   *

Public health and inventiveness are closely linked. Such administrative virtuosity is always in demand. Cure of 20,000,000 anticipating the blindness of onchocerciasis, escape for the hundred millions still threatened by malaria, relief for the 70,-000 afflicted annually with cholera, rests with imaginative men and the international organizations they serve. (See appendices for partial list.)

A single national effort is seldom adequate today. The nations most in need are least able to deal with broad health problems, and absence of disease alone does not mean health. An area's health involves food, clean water, education, disease prevention and therapy and control. Prosperous western nations can usually provide for themselves. The fledgling countries cannot. In addition, what is done in one must be done in neighboring areas. What good, say, is black fly control in Upper Volta if black flies are not also attacked in nearby Ghana? Only the international organizations can help where national efforts are not enough. This is a universally acknowledged fact. Of all matters debated among nations, the value of international health effort is debated least.

Until mid-19th century there was no international public health, most authorities hold that the first true international public health effort was inspired only by the arrival of cholera in western Europe at about this time. This was the International Sanitary Conference called July 23, 1851, in Paris, the first of six well-meant but hamstrung meetings between nations during the last century.

Choice of nations summoned to this first conference reflected an attitude toward the world, namely that it was primarily a European one. The nations in attendance were European and some no longer exist except as historical names: Austria, France, Greece, the Papal States, Portugal, Russia, Sardinia, the Two Sicilies, Spain, Turkey, Tuscany, and England.

All hoped to hammer out some agreement on minimum maritime quarantine requirements (for cholera particularly), and also, as the conference president stated, "render important services to the trade and shipping of the Mediterranean, while at the same time safeguarding public health.''

The conference ended January 19, 1852, and all 12 conferees did reach agreement, an ambitious paper stipulating 137 measures convering cholera and other matters. It became useless the day the conference closed because only three countries ratified, two of which later withdrew.

Time passed, as did other cooperative efforts.

One hundred and twenty years after the first sanitary convention the newest refinement in international health efforts is WHO, headquarters Geneva. WHO is the specialized public health agency of the United Nations and is held by many to be the best possible instrument for its job at this time.

WHO is not the first international health organization, but membership, aims, and capability are larger than any of its predecessors. It has inherited functions (and frustrations) of several ancestral groups such as the Health Organization of the League of Nations, the Office International d'Hygiene Publique, and the Health Division of the United Nations, Relief and Rehabilitation Administration.

A world health organization was proposed at the first United Nations conference in San Francisco in 1945. In 1946, representatives of 61 governments met at the International Health Conference in New York City, drafted the WHO constitution (see appendices), and formed an interim commission to serve until the required 26 United Nations member states could ratify it. Ratification took place on April 7, 1948. The date is celebrated annually as World Health Day. The first World Health Assembly convened in Geneva at the Palais des Nations in June, 1948. On September 1, 1948, the permanent World Health Organization came into being. There are 126 member states today, and three associate members.

WHO's tasks are administered by three bodies: The World Health Assembly which is WHO's supreme authority, an executive board, and a secretariat. As described by *The World Health Organization*, WHO publication outlining its own workings:

> . . . The World Health Assembly, its governing body, is composed of delegates of member states, each of which has one vote. At the annual three-week meeting of the assembly, health policy is established, the work of the past year is reviewed, and the program

and budget for the following year is adopted. Each year it elects eight member states to designate a person to serve for three years on the 24-member executive board and to replace the eight retiring members. The board meets at least twice a year and acts as the executive organ of the Assembly, giving effect to its decisions, advising on technical questions, and dealing with emergencies, such as epidemics, earthquakes and floods, where immediate action is required. To meet the health needs of different areas, WHO has established six regional organizations, each with a regional committee composed of member states and associate members. (Regional committees are: Africa, Americas, Southeast Asia, Europe, Eastern Mediterranean, Western Pacific.) The directing council of the Pan American Health Organization serves as the WHO regional committee for the Americas. Regional committees meet once a year to review health work in their respective areas and plan continuation and development. Regional plans are amalgamated into overall plans for the organization by the director general at WHO's headquarters in Geneva and submitted to the Executive Board and the Health Assembly.

WHO programs, services to governments, and general technical services are financed by an annual budget allotment, voluntary contributions from individual nations and other organizations, a UN Development Program Fund and the UN Children's Fund (UNICEF).

The World Health Assembly establishes WHO's yearly budget, $51,515,000 in 1967, [$55,000,000 in 1968] including $2,415,000 for the first year of the smallpox eradication program. The budget is financed by several sources, one being assessments levied against WHO member nations. 1967 contributions ranged from $21,-320 to $16,627,320.

＊　　　＊　　　＊

WHO gives nothing away. The impression that WHO does so must often be corrected. Typical is the question asked by a reporter one day in fall of 1967: "Is it true that WHO will give intrauterine devices to any country asking for them?" The answer was "No." The reporter was told, however, that the

WHO supply department would purchase IUDs for any country requesting that it do so, and at the lowest possible price. WHO supply has purchased Japanese motorcycles for member countries. It has moved research monkeys impounded for taxes by deducting the taxes from the supplier's profits. It has remarked to drug countries loathe to submit supply bids to small countries that they might not be asked to submit bids to large countries in the future, either, if they did not comply.

Frank Wilson, WHO supply services chief, said, "We must frequently make the distinction clear. These are all WHO-assisted projects, not WHO giveaway programs. WHO sends technical advisers, but doesn't take upon itself the job of supplying. If a country wants material aid in addition to personnel, we purchase for them on a reimbursable basis. WHO could not afford to give material away, and does not believe it doing so. WHO believes that a country will put more value on something it must purchase for itself. But . . . when WHO makes a purchase, you can be sure it is at the lowest possible price for the highest quality merchandise." This is not exaggeration. The UN represents the world. When the UN makes a request, commercial interests, at least, lend a polite ear.

The scope of WHO's work exceeds that of any previous international health body. It must. There is more public health work going on in the 1960s than at any time in history: control of malaria, tuberculosis, venereal and other communicable diseases, maternal and child health, mental health, social and occupational health, nutrition, nursing, environmental sanitation, public health administration, professional education and training, mass public health education.

WHO is also involved in global technical projects:
- Compilation of an international pharamacopoeia.
- Establishing standards against which antibiotics, vaccines, and blood serum can be measured.
- Addictive drug control.
- Collection and broadcast of epidemiological information.

It is demonstrable fact that such a work load is beyond the talent of any single nation.

＊　　＊　　＊

It is also demonstrable that only the international organizations can provide for the future.

In immunology the greatest need is research, on African diseases in general, said Dr. Howard Goodman, WHO immunology section chief late in 1967. There were barely a dozen places in the entire world investigating malaria immunity at that time. WHO wants at least seven immunology centers established in regions where communicable diseases take heaviest toll, one reason being to train students in their own countries. The first opened in 1964 in University College Hospital, Ibadan, Nigeria.

In surveillance, with progress in epidemiology and new laboratory methods, it may be possible to predict the coming of communicable diseases anywhere in the world, and which members of a population will contract them. Success here depends entirely on dovetailed international efforts.

In insect vector control, geneticists may be able to breed a distaste for man into mosquitoes, a step toward eradicating malaria and yellow fever.

In the future too there will appear diseases which appear to be new though they may or may not be, and which will not be the problem of any one country because they strike in many. Haemorrhagic fever is one, a mosquito-borne, virus-caused scourge which first appeared in Manila in 1954. It resembles dengue fever. No vaccine has yet been developed that is considered suitable for use in epidemic areas, and apart from mosquito control, there are no other control measures known. Figures cited by Dr. A.C. Saenz, medical officer of WHO's virus diseases unit, show the disease concentrates on children and kills one in every ten victims.

One of the staggering problems of the future has nothing to do with health and disease at all. As described by Dr. Marcolino G. Candau, WHO's director general, in *The Work of WHO, 1966*, his annual report to the World Health Assembly and to the UN, the problem is an old, familiar one:

> The supreme challenge in 1966 to all intergovernmental organizations in the UN family continued to be the widening gap separating the developing countries from the technologically and economically more developed. . . .
>
> Most of the factors . . . also apply to international health work. They include on the one hand, inability or unwillingness of the economically more fortunate nations to adjust aid, financial and otherwise, to the constantly expanding needs of the developing countries; and, on the other, political instability and unrest

in many of the areas concerned, administrative ineffic-
iency, and the absence of well-established, and realistic
planning processes. . . .

As a result, WHO in 1966 was able to make disappointingly little headway in assisting developing countries to establish and strengthen even basic national
health services.

*   *   *

Clever individuals will still be necessary, no matter how
global the efforts become. Case after case from the field offers
proof.

For example, residents of one Indian village refused to use
the brand new latrines built for them by a WHO-assisted water
supply team. For months they stood empty. No one among
the builders understood why and the villagers themselves would
not speak about it. One of the team members finally understood. The villagers were Moslems. The new latrines faced
Mecca. Moslems will not move their bowels while facing the
Holy City.

In a Brazilian village, new washtubs were likewise ignored,
and the engineer who built them likewise understood. Washing
at the river was a social occasion, a time for gossip. The new
basins were situated in a line; women using them could not
face one another to talk. This intuitive engineer then uprooted
the basins and reset them in circular clusters. The women
never washed in the river again.

In India, an antiplague group found its rat traps empty
several days in succession. Members were baffled. The traps
were well made and had never failed. After several days of
investigation, team members suddenly guessed why and they
were correct. Many Buddhists lived in the plague area. Budd-
hist belief rules all life sacred. Therefore men must not kill
rats and must save them from being killed by others. The
Buddhists had been opening the traps at night.

The plague people solved the problem with a watchman;
he stood over the traps with a long pole. With the stick he
rapped those who came near, yet, never came close enough to
the trap himself to scare off the rats.

Once again, it is easier to understand things so large in
terms of the individuals involved with them. This is true with
WHO. "I'm not in WHO because the work is easy, and I'm
not in it because the work is fun," a child care nurse once
explained. "I'm in it because I think the work is worth while."

ANNEXES

MEMBERS AND ASSOCIATE MEMBERS OF THE
WORLD HEALTH ORGANIZATION
as of 31 December 1967

At 31 December 1967 the World Health Organization had 126 Member States and associate members. They are listed below, with a date on which each became a party to the constitution or the date of admission to associate membership.

Afghanistan	19 April 1948
Albania	26 May 1947
Algeria*	8 November 1962
Argentina*	22 October 1948
Australia*	2 February 1948
Austria*	30 June 1947
Barbados	25 June 1967
Belgium*	25 June 1948
Bolivia	23 December 1949
Brazil*	2 June 1948
Bulgaria	9 June 1948
Burma	1 July 1948
Burundi	22 October 1962
Byelorussian SSR	7 April 1948
Cambodia*	17 May 1950
Cameroon	6 May 1960
Canada*	29 August 1946
Central African Republic*	20 September 1960
Ceylon	7 July 1948
Chad	1 January 1961
Chile*	15 October 1948
China	22 July 1946
Columbia	14 May 1959
Congo (Brazzaville)	26 October 1960
Congo, Democratic Republic of	24 February 1961
Costa Rica	17 March 1949
Cuba	9 May 1950
Cyprus*	16 January 1961
Czechoslovakia*	1 March 1948
Dahomey	20 September 1960
Denmark*	19 April 1948

Dominican Republic	21 June 1948
Ecuador*	1 March 1949
El Salvador	22 June 1948
Ethiopia	11 April 1947
Federal Republic of Germany*	29 May 1951
Finland*	7 October 1947
France	16 June 1948
Gabon	21 November 1960
Ghana*	8 April 1957
Greece	12 March 1948
Guatemala*	26 August 1949
Guinea	19 May 1959
Guyana	27 September 1966
Haiti*	12 August 1947
Honduras	8 April 1949
Hungary	17 June 1948
Iceland	17 June 1948
India*	12 January 1948
Indonesia	23 May 1950
Iran	23 November 1946
Iraq*	23 September 1947
Ireland	20 October 1947
Israel	21 June 1949
Italy*	11 April 1947
Ivory Coast*	28 October 1960
Jamaica*	21 March 1963
Japan*	16 May 1951
Jordan*	7 April 1947
Kenya*	27 January 1964
Kuwait*	9 May 1960
Laos*	17 May 1950
Lebanon	19 January 1949
Lesotho	7 July 1967
Liberia	14 March 1947
Libya*	16 May 1952
Luxembourg*	3 June 1949
Madagascar*	16 January 1961
Malawi*	9 April 1965
Malaysia*	24 April 1958
Maldive Islands	5 November 1965
Mali	17 October 1960
Malta	1 February 1965

Mauritania	7 March 1961
Mexico	7 April 1948
Monaco	8 July 1948
Mongolia	18 April 1962
Morocco*	14 May 1956
Nepal*	2 September 1953
Netherlands*	25 April 1947
New Zealand*	10 December 1946
Nicaragua*	24 April 1950
Niger	5 October 1960
Nigeria*	25 November 1960
Norway*	18 August 1947
Pakistan*	23 June 1948
Panama	20 February 1951
Paraguay	4 January 1949
Peru	11 November 1949
Philippines*	9 July 1948
Poland	6 May 1948
Portugal	13 February 1948
Republic of Korea	17 August 1949
Romania	8 June 1948
Rwanda*	7 November 1962
Saudi Arabia	26 May 1947
Senegal*	31 October 1960
Sierra Leone*	20 October 1961
Singapore*	25 February 1966
Somalia	26 January 1961
South Africa	7 August 1947
Spain	28 May 1951
Sudan	14 May 1956
Sweden*	28 August 1947
Switzerland	26 March 1947
Syria	18 December 1946
Thailand*	26 September 1947
Togo*	13 May 1960
Trinidad and Tobago*	3 January 1963
Tunisia*	14 May 1956
Turkey	2 January 1948
Uganda	7 March 1963
Ukrainian SSR	3 April 1948
Union of Soviet Socialist Republics*	24 March 1948
United Arab Republic*	16 December 1947

United Kingdom of Great Britain and Northern Ireland	22 July 1946
United Republic of Tanzania*	15 March 1962
United States	21 June 1948
Upper Volta*	4 October 1960
Uruguay	22 April 1949
Venezuela	7 July 1948
Vietnam	17 May 1950
Western Samoa	16 May 1962
Yemen	20 November 1953
Yugoslavia*	19 November 1947
Zambia	2 February 1965

Associate Members

Mauritius	9 May 1963
Qatar	5 March 1964
Southern Rhodesia	16 May 1950

*Member states that have acceded to the Convention on the Privileges and Immunities of the Specialized Agencies and its Annex VII.

IMPORTANT NONGOVERNMENTAL ORGANIZATIONS
IN OFFICIAL RELATIONS WITH WHO
as of 31 December 1967

Biometric Society
Central Council for Health Education
Council for International Organizations of Medical Sciences
Inter-American Association of Sanitary Engineering
International Academy of Legal Medicine and of Social Medicine
International Air Transport Association
International Association for Child Psychiatry and Allied Pro-
fessions
International Association of Logopedics and Phoniatrics
International Association of Microbiological Societies
International Association for Prevention of Blindness
International Astronautical Federation
International Brain Research Organization
International Commission on Radiological Protection
International Commission on Radiation Units and Measurements
International Committee of Catholic Nurses
International Committee of the Red Cross
International Confederation of Midwives
International Conference of Social Work
International Council on Jewish Social and Welfare Services
International Council of Nurses
International Council of Scientific Unions
International Council of Societies of Pathology
International Dental Federation
International Diabetes Federation
International Epidemiological Association
International Federation of Gynecology and Obstetrics
International Federation for Housing and Planning
International Federal for Medical and Biological Engineering
International Federation of Physical Medicine
International Federation of Sports Medicine
International Federation of Surgical Colleges
International Fertility Association
International Hospital Federation
International Hydatidological Association
International League of Dermatological Societies

International League Against Rheumatism
International Leprosy Association
International Organization Against Trachoma
International Pediatric Association
International Pharmaceutical Federation
International Planned Parenthood Federation
International Society of Biometeorology
International Society of Blood Transfusion
International Society of Cardiology
International Society of Criminology
International Society for Rehabilitation of the Disabled
International Union of Architects
International Union Against Cancer
International Union for Child Welfare
International Union for Health Education
International Union of Local Authorities
International Union of Pure and Applied Chemistry
International Union Against Tuberculosis
International Union Against the Venereal Diseases and the
    Treponematoses
International Water Supply Association
League of Red Cross Societies
Medical Women's International Association
Permanent Commission and International Association on Occupa-
    tional Health
World Federation for Physical Therapy
World Federation of the Deaf
World Federation for Mental Health
World Federation of Neurology
World Federation of Occupational Therapists
World Federation of Societies of Anesthesiologists
World Federation of United Nations Associations
World Medical Association
World Psychiatric Association
World Union OSE
World Veterans Federation
World Veterinary Association

ANNEX THREE

INTERNATIONAL PUBLIC HEALTH CONFERENCES AND CONVENTIONS ON COMMUNICABLE DISEASES IN THE 19th AND 20th CENTURIES PRIOR TO FOUNDING OF THE WORLD HEALTH ORGANIZATION

1851, Paris—The very first international sanitary conference was held. An agreement was signed by some nations, then ignored.

1859, Paris—A conference and draft agreement only.

1866, Istanbul—First plan and regulations for the Mecca pilgrimages were drawn.

1874, Vienna—Proposal was made for an international epidemic commission. Inspection and surveillance was also recommended in place of general quarantine.

1881, Washington—Notification of communicable disease outbreaks was recommended, via international clearing houses.

1885, Rome—Miscellaneous recommendations were made, mostly concerning cholera.

1892, Venice—The first effective but limited international convention was signed. Its provisions covered the Mecca pilgrimage only.

1893, Dresden—A general convention on cholera was drawn and signed.

1894, Paris—Mecca pilgrimage provisions and Dresden convention (above) were broadened. New provisions were disregarded.

1897, Venice—A new convention was drawn. It included international plague control provisions. Agreements on international communicable disease notifications were reaffirmed. The 1893 Dresden agreements were ratified.

1903, Paris—A modern convention covering plague and cholera was drawn and signed by 20 nations.

1907, Rome—The *Office International d'Hygiéne* was established by international agreement.

1912, Paris—The 1903 convention was broadened to include international yellow fever control.

1926, Paris—The same convention was broadened still further to cover typhus and smallpox and is still observed substantially.

1933—A convention spelling out air travel regulations plus an agreement was signed without calling a formal conference. This is also still observed.

1938, Paris—On the eve of World War Two amendments were made to the 1926 convention, resulting from shutdown of the Sanitary, Maritime, and Quarantine Board of Egypt.

1944—Two conventions were signed, further modifying those of 1926 and 1933, above, without a full dress conference to first discuss them. The two measures were sponsored by the United Nations Relief and Rehabilitation Administration.

1946, New York—The World Health Organization constitution was drawn and signed. In it WHO is defined as "the directing and coordinating authority on international health work."

1948, New York—The WHO constitution was ratified on April 8, establishing WHO as an independent international health agency, its relationship with the United Nations governed by its own constitution, the UN charter, and other agreements.

*   *   *

Note: The International Sanitary Regulations, in effect today, were adopted by the Fourth World Health Assembly in 1951 in Geneva. The International Sanitary Regulations cover all forms of global transport, that is, ships, aircraft, trains, and motor vehicles. They spell out the sanitary conditions to be maintained and measures to be taken at international sea and air terminals. They specify regulations to be followed on arrival and departure, sanitation methods and sanitation certificates. The regulations are observed by all the world's nations and cover the six communicable infections known as "Internationally Quarantinable Diseases": cholera, plague, relapsing fever, smallpox, typhus, yellow fever.

A new set of regulations, designed to fit new conditions created by jumbo jets, and containerization is under study.

CRITERIA FOR THE CERTIFICATION OF
MALARIA ERADICATION

The 13th World Health Assembly in resolution WHA. 13.55 requested the director general "to establish an official register listing areas where malaria eradication has been achieved after inspection and certification by a WHO evaluation team." The task of inspection and certification is entrusted to an evaluation team set up by the relevant regional office of WHO. The team visits the area for which certification has been requested by the government, and the names of its members appear in the certification report. The criteria to be met in order to obtain certification of malaria eradication as set out by the WHO Expert Committee on Malaria are as follows:

(1) Proof that an adequate surveillance system has operated in the area for at least three years, in at least two of which no specific anopheline control measures have been carried out; any claim based on a lesser period of postoperational surveillance would need to be supported by proof of a surveillance mechanism above the usual quality.

(2) Evidence that in this period of three years no indigenous cases, originating within that time, have been discovered.

(3) The evidence of a register of malaria infections discovered during that time, it being established beyond reasonable doubt that each case was either:

(a) Imported, as shown by the tracing of the case to its origin in an acknowledged malarious area; or

(b) A relapse of a pre-existing infection, as shown by the history of the case, and the absence of any associated cases in the neighborhood of its origin; or

(c) Induced, as shown by its relation to a blood transfusion within an appropriate interval or to another form of parenteral inoculation to which infection could be properly attributed; or

(d) Directly secondary to a known imported case; or

(e) Cryptic, that is, isolated and not associated with secondary cases, as determined through appropriate epidemiological investigation, including mass blood survey after the expiry of the incubation intervals.

THE MOSQUITO LEGEND –
A TALE OF SOUTH VIETNAM

Once upon a time there was a happy young couple. They loved one another dearly. But Fate was envious of their bliss and one day sent Death to take the young wife away.

Overwhelmed with grief, the husband would not think of burying her. But the work of Death is the same for everyone and her body began to return to dust. The sight was too much for the villagers and, rather than part from his wife, the young man chose to go away. He became a pariah rejected by everybody and went to live on the river, leaving his sampan only to fetch food from the nearest village.

Finally, because of his stubborn will to keep the object of his love, the genies took pity on him. One of them appeared to him as he was drifting on the river in deep grief and despair. "It is in my power to help you," the genie said, "but you should know that it is not always wise to change one's destiny. You should learn to accept your fate. However, if you really want it, I shall make your wife live again . . . I hope you will not live to regret it."

The husband said that this was his fondest hope. He would never have regrets.

"Let it be done as you wish," the genie said. He pricked the man's finger letting out a drop of blood which fell on the dead body of the girl. And lo, she was alive again, as beautiful as ever.

The young couple decided to continue living on the river. But one night, coming back from the village where he had gone for food, the husband could not find his lovely wife. The sampan was empty. She was gone. He called for her but she did not answer. Yet he had not far to go to find her. She had left home to live with a man on a boat nearby. Her husband begged her to return, but it was of no avail. She did not want to come back. She would simply follow her will.

He tried to tell her how ungrateful she was. Was it not to him that she owed her second life?

Standing on the prow of the next sampan, the young woman answered him crossly. They argued a long time. In the end she said she would have no more to do with him. He could have his drop of blood back.

She snatched a long pin from her hair and pricked her finger. A pearl of blood sprang out and rolled into the river. With it went the life that her husband had given back to her. Her body fell again into dust and drifted gently on the water. Slowly, the dust changed into tiny grubs, from which mosquitoes were born.

The husband then remembered the words of the genie. He did not weep for his unfaithful wife. He married again and had many children, from whom we all descend.

As for the faithless one, she cannot overcome her anger and grief. She has been changed into a mosquito. She harasses mankind with her buzzing, thus expressing her sorrow, and she stings us trying to steal back the drop of blood which would give her life again.

REFERENCES

GENERAL

Anderson, Gaylord W., Margaret Arnstein, and Mary Lester, Communicable Disease Control, 4th edition, New York, Macmillan Company, 1962.

Bierstein, Paul, "The Community Watersupply Program of the World Health Organization," mimeographed document, dated May, 1967, in the World Health Organization Library, Geneva.

Calder, Ritchie, Ten steps Forward—World Health 1948-1958, Geneva, World Health Organization, 1958.

Castiglioni, Arturo, A History of Medicine, 2nd edition, translated from the Italian and edited by E. B. Krumbhaar, New York, Alfred A. Knopf, 1958.

Dewhurst, Kenneth, Dr. Thomas Sydenham (1624-1689), Berkeley, California, and Los Angeles, University of California Press, 1966.

First Ten Years of the World Health Organization, The, Geneva, World Health Organization, 1958.

Garrison, Fielding H., An Introduction to the History of Medicine, 4th edition reprinted, Philadelphia, London, W.B. Saunders Company, 1966.

Genetics of Vectors and Insecticide Resistance—Report of a WHO Scientific Group, World Health Organization Technical Report Series No. 268, 1964.

Goodman, Neville M., International Health Organizations and Their Work, Philadelphia, New York, Blakiston Company, 1952.

Guthrie, Douglas, History of Medicine, Philadelphia, J.B. Lippincott Company, 1946.

Haggard, Howard W., Devils, Drugs and Doctors, New York, London, Harper and Brothers, 1929.

Heiser, Victor, An American Doctor's Odyssey, New York, W.W. Norton and Company, 1936.

Hemming, James, Mankind Against the Killers, London, New York, Toronto, Longmans, Green and Company, 1958.

Hirsch, August, Handbook of Geographical and Historical Pathology, translated by C. Creighton, I, II, London, The New Sydenham Society, 1885.

Inglis, Brian, A History of Medicine, Cleveland, New York, World Publishing Company, 1965.

Lapage, Geoffrey, Man Against Disease, London, New York, Toronto, Abelard Schuman, 1964.

Major, Ralph, A History of Medicine, I, Springfield, Illinois, Charles C. Thomas, 1954.

Marriott, Henry J.L., Medical Milestones, Baltimore, Williams and Wilkins Company, 1952.

Marti-Ibanez, Felix, The Crystal Arrow, New York, Clarkson N. Potter, Inc., 1964.

New York Bible Society, The Holy Bible, King James version.

Pal, R., "Genetics of Insect Vectors of Disease," World Health Organization Chronicle, 21 (August, 1967), pp. 343-350.

"Problems of Immunology Today," World Health Organization Chronicle, 19 (March, 1965), pp. 91-101.

Rapport, S., and Helen Wright, editors, Great Adventures in Medicine, New York, Dial Press, 1952.

Raska, Karel, "National and International Surveillance of Communicable Diseases," World Health Organization Chronicle, 20 (September, 1966), pp. 315-321.

Role of Immunization in Communicable Disease Control, The, Public Health Papers No. 8, Geneva, World Health Organization, 1961.

Roueché, Berton, Field Guide to Disease—A Handbook for World Travelers, Boston, Toronto, Little, Brown and Company, 1967.

Sambasivan, G., Halfdan Mahler, Thorstein Guthe, W. Ferreira, A.C. Saenz, S.G. Drozdov, F. Maxwell-Lyons, B. Cvjetanovic, L.M. Bechelli, and N. Ansari, "World Fight Against Communicable Diseases: A Progress Report," World Health, (May, 1966), pp. 3-11.

Second Ten Years of the World Health Organization, The, Geneva, World Health Organization, 1968.

Sigerist, Henry E., A History of Medicine—Early Greek, Hindu, and Persian Medicine, II, New York, Oxford University Press, 1961.

Sigerist, Henry E., Civilization and Disease, Ithaca, Cornell University Press, 1943.

Styler, Herman, Plague Fighters, Philadelphia, New York, Chilton Company, 1960.

Third Report on the World Health Situation 1961-1964, Official Records of the World Health Organization No. 155, Geneva, World Health Organization, 1967.

Top, Franklyn H., Communicable Diseases, 3rd edition, St. Louis, C.V. Mosby Company, 1955.

Top, Franklyn H., and others, Communicable and Infectious Diseases: Diagnosis, Prevention, and Treatment, 5th edition, St. Louis, C.V. Mosby Company, 1964.

"Water," subject of entire issue, World Health, (July-August, 1964).

Work of WHO 1965, The—Annual Report of the Director General to the World Health Assembly and to the United Nations, Official Records of the World Health Organization No. 147, Geneva, World Health Organization, 1966.

Work of WHO, 1966, The—Annual Report of the Director General to the World Health Assembly and to the United Nations, Official Records of the World Health Organization No. 156, Geneva, World Health Organization, 1967.

Work of WHO, 1967, The—Annual Report of the Director General to the World Health Assembly and to the United Nations, Official Records of the World Health Organization No. 164, Geneva, World Health Organization, 1968.

WHO Expert Committee on Cholera, Second Report, World Health Organization Technical Report Series No. 352, 1967.

Wright, J.W., and R. Pal, editors, Genetics of Insect Vectors of Disease, Amsterdam, London, New York, Elsevier Publishing Company, 1967.

Zinsser, Hans, Rats, Lice and History, Boston, Toronto, Little, Brown and Company, 1935.

*   *   *

See generally the following publications. *Note:* Certain editions containing pertinent articles appearing in them are already specified in the subject reference above and following.

Bulletin of the World Health Organization, Geneva, World Health Organization (1960 to present).

International Journal of Health Education, Geneva, Studer S.A. (1958 to present).

Rural Health Digest—A Collection of Reports, Experiences, and Ideas Leading to Rural Health Development, New Delhi, S.E. Asia Regional Office of the World Health Organization (1959-1963).

World Health—The Magazine of the World Health Organization, Geneva, World Health Organization (1960 to present).

World Health Organization Chronicle, Geneva, World Health Organization (1960 to present).

CHOLERA

Forbes, G.I., J.D.F. Lockart, and R.K. Bowman, "Cholera and Nightsoil Infection in Hong Kong, 1966," Bulletin of the World Health Organization, 36 (1967), pp. 367-373.

Kirimly, H., "Mecca Pilgrimage," World Health, (August-September, 1967), pp. 10-13.

Longmate, Norman, King Cholera—The Biography of a Disease, London, Hamish Hamilton Ltd., 1966.

MacNamara, Charles N., A History of Asiatic Cholera, London, Macmillan and Company, 1876.

Pollitzer, Robert, Cholera, World Health Organization Monograph Series No. 43, Geneva, World Health Organization, 1959.

Rosenberg, Charles E., The Cholera Years—The U.S. in 1832, 1849 and 1966, Chicago, University of Chicago Press, 1962.

Snow, John, "The Broad Street Pump," in Curiosities of Medicine, edited by Berton Roueché, Boston, Toronto, Little, Brown and Company, 1963, pp. 69-76.

Thapalyal, Lalit, "Millions of Pilgrims in the Shadows of Cholera," World Health, (January-February, 1961), pp. 24-25.

INFLUENZA

Burnet, F.M., and E. Clark, Influenza, Walter and Eliza Hall Institute of Research, monograph four, Melbourne, Macmillan and Company, 1942.

Creighton, Charles, A History of Epidemics in Britain, I, II, Cambridge, Cambridge University Press, 1891-94.

Hoehling, A.A., The Great Epidemic —When the Spanish Influenza Struck, Boston, Toronto, Little, Brown and Company, 1961.

Influenza—A Review of Current Research by Various Authors, World Health Organization Monograph Series No. 20, Geneva, World Health Organization, 1954.

Slepuskin, A.N., T.K. Bobyleva, A.E. Russina, B.S. Vitkina, N.S. Ellengorn, and V.M. Zdanov, "Evaluation of the Effectiveness of Large Scale Vaccination Against Influenza in the USSR," Bulletin of the World Health Organization, 36 (1967), pp. 385-395.

Stuart-Harris, C.H., "Influenza," in The History and Conquest of Common Diseases, edited by Walter Bett, Norman, University of Oklahoma Press, 1954, pp. 71-83.

Zdanov, V.M., M.K. Nesterenko, I.V. Antonova, A.S. Gorbunova, V.A. Isacenko, and I.A. Krasovskaja, "The 1965 A2 Influenza Epidemic in the USSR and the Natural History of Asian Influenza," Bulletin of the World Health Organization, 34 (1966), pp. 877-884.

LEPROSY

Bechelli, L.M., and V. Martinez Dominquez, A Guide to Leprosy Control, mimeographed document, Geneva, World Health Organization, 1966.

Bechelli, L.M., and V. Martinez Dominquez, "The Leprosy Problem in the World," Bulletin of the World Health Organization, 34 (1966), pp. 811-826.

Brown, J.A. Kinnear, and M.M. Stone, "BCG Vaccination of Children Against Leprosy: First Results of a Trial in Uganda," British Medical Journal, 1 (1966), pp. 7-14. With an appendix by Dr. Ian Sutherland.

Christian Medical Fellowship, Biblical Leprosy—A suggested Interpretation, 2nd edition, London, Tyndale Press, 1963.

Lowe, J., "Comments on the History of Leprosy," Indian Medical Gazette, 77 (1942), p. 680. Reprinted in Leprosy Review, 18 (1947), p. 54.

Mumm, Elizabeth, "Preliminary Comments on a Study of Prejudices and Negative Attitudes Related to Leprosy in Two Geographic Areas in Korea," mimeographed document WPR/Leprosy/41, dated May 5, 1965, in the World Health Organization Library, Geneva, compiled for First Regional Seminar on Leprosy Control, Manila, Philippines, April 21-28, 1965.

Newell, Kenneth, W., "An Epidemiologist's View of Leprosy," Bulletin of the World Health Organization, 34 (1966), pp. 827-857.

Roueché, Berton, "A Lonely Road," in 11 Blue Men, anthology by Berton Roueché, Boston, Toronto, Little, Brown and Company, 1953, pp. 121-141.

PARASITES: Malaria

Alvarado, Carlos, and L.J. Bruce-Chwatt, "Malaria," Scientific American, (May, 1962), pp. 86-98.

Bruce-Chwatt, L.J. "Malaria," in Cecil-Loeb's "A Textbook of Medicine," 12th edition, edited by Paul B. Beeson and Walsh McDermott, Philadelphia and London, W.B. Saunders Company, 1967, pp. 350-362.

Chemotherapy of Malaria—Report of a Technical Meeting, World Health Organization Technical Report Series No. 226, 1961.

Gramiccia, G., "Lessions Learned During the Final Stages of Malaria Eradication in Europe," *Rivista di Parassitologia*, XXV (September, 1964), pp. 157-167.

Jaramillo Arango, Jaime, Conquest of Malaria, London, Heinemann, 1950.

Malaria Eradication—A Plea for Health, 2nd edition, Geneva, World Health Organization, 1959.

Mineau, Wayne, The Fever Peaks, London, Peter Davies Ltd., 1962.

Pampana, Emilio, A Textbook of Malaria Eradication, London, Oxford University Press, 1963.

Russell, Paul F., Man's Mastery of Malaria, London, Oxford, University Press, 1955.

Russell, P.F., L.S. West, R.D. Manwell, and G. Macdonald, Practical Malariology, London, Oxford University Press, 1963.

Terminology of Malaria and Malaria Eradication, Geneva, World Health Organization, 1963.

WHO Expert Committee on Malaria, 13th Report, World Health Organization Technical Report Series No. 357, 1967.

PARASITES: Bilharziasis

Chemotherapy of Bilharziasis—Report of a WHO Scientific Group, World Health Organization Technical Report Series No. 317, 1966.

Epidemiology and Control of Schistosomiasis—Report of a WHO Expert Committee, World Health Organization Technical Report Series No. 372, 1967.

Farooq, M., "Historical Development," mimeographed document BILH/WP/66.1, dated 1966, in the World Health Organization Library, Geneva.

Measurement of the Public Health Importance of Bilharziasis—Report of a WHO Scientific Group, World Health Organization Technical Report Series No. 349, 1967.

Molluscicides—Second Report of the Expert Committee on Bilharziasis, World Health Organization Technical Report Series No. 214, 1961.

Roueché, Berton, "A Swim in the Nile," in A Man Named Hoffman, anthology by Berton Roueche, Boston, Toronto, Little, Brown and Company, 1965, pp. 236-256.

"Some Characteristics of Immunity in Parasitic Diseases," Immunology and Parasitic Diseases—Report of a WHO Expert Committee, World Health Organization Technical Report Series No. 315, 1965, pp. 28-32.

WHO Expert Committee on Bilharziasis, Third Report, World Health Organization Technical Report Series No. 299, 1965.

"World United Against Malaria, The," subject of extra issue, World Health, (undated).

PARASITES: *Onchocerciasis*

Erlich, David A., "River Blindness Afflicts 200,000,000," Science News, (July 1, 1967), pp. 16-17.

Parasitic Diseases Unit, Division of Communicable Diseases, World Health Organization, Onchocerciasis, Its Public Health Importance and Prospect of Control, duplicated document, dated 1967, in the World Health Organization Library, Geneva.

"Tropical River Blindness," World Health, (March-April, 1962), pp. 16-17.

WHO Expert Committee on Onchocerciasis, Second Report, World Health Organization Technical Report Series No. 335, 1966.

"WHO Steps Up Campaign Against River Blindness," World Medicine, (July 18, 1967), pp. 29-30.

PLAGUE

Gray, Thomas J., "Meet the Rat," subject of entire issue, World Health, (April, 1967).

Lyle, David, "Plague and War, 1966," Esquire, (September, 1966), pp. 158-162.

Nohl, Johannes, The Black Death—A Chronicle of the Plague, compiled from contemporary sources and translated by C.H. Clarke, London, George Allen and Unwin Ltd., 1926.

Pollitzer, Robert, Plague, World Health Organization Monograph Series No. 22, Geneva, World Health Organization, 1954.

SMALLPOX

Creighton, Charles, A History of Epidemics in Britain, I, Cambridge, Cambridge University Press, 1891, pp. 439-445.

Fracastoro, Girolamo, De contagione et Contagiosis Morbis et Eorum Curatione, Libri III, translation and notes by Wilmer Cave Wright, New York, G.P. Putnam's Sons 1930.

Handbook for Smallpox Eradication Programs in Endemic Areas, mimeographed document SE/67.5 Rev. 1, Geneva, World Health Organization, 1967.

Rosen, George, "Acute Communicable Diseases—[includes] Small-pox," in The History and Conquest of Common Diseases, edited by Walter Bett, Norman, University of Oklahoma Press, 1954, pp. 47-57.

Roueché, Berton, "A Man from Mexico," in 11 Blue Men, anthology by Berton Roueche, Boston, Toronto, Little, Brown and Company, 1953, pp. 100-120.

"Smallpox," subject of entire issue, World Health (March, 1965).

Smallpox Eradication Unit, World Health Organization, Small-pox Eradication Surveillance Report No. 1, mimeographed document SE/SR/67.1, dated September, 1967, in World Health Organization Library, Geneva.

WHO Expert Committee on Smallpox, First Report, World Health Organization Technical Report Series No. 283, 1964.

SYPHILIS

Cawadias, A.P., "The Venereal Diseases," in The History and Conquests of Common Diseases, edited by Walter Bett, Norman, University of Oklahoma Press, 1954, pp. 178-188.

Guthe, Thorstein, "Endemic Treponematoses of Childhood," in International Work in Endemic Treponematoses and Venereal Infections 1948-1963, Geneva, World Health Organization, 1965, pp. 5-19.

King, Ambrose, "Venereal Disease Among Young People," World Health Organization Chronicle, 19 (April, 1965), pp. 144-148.

Sudhoff, Karl, The Earliest Printed Literature on Syphilis. Being Ten Tractates from the Years 1495-1498, adapted by Charles Singer, Florence, R. Lier and Company, 1925.

"Venereal Syphilis," in International Work in Endemic Treponematoses and Venereal Infections 1948-1963, Geneva, World Health Organization, 1965, pp. 20-31.

"Why Has Syphilis Returned?" World Health, (November, 1964), pp. 36-37.

TUBERCULOSIS

Burke, Richard M., Historical Chronology of Tuberculosis, Springfield, Illinois, Charles C. Thomas, 1955.

Calmette, Leon, Tuberculosis in Man and Animals, Baltimore, Williams and Wilkins Company, 1923.

Diagnostic Standards and Classification of Tuberculosis, New York, National Tuberculosis Association, 1961.

Cummins, Stevenson L., Tuberculosis in History—from the 17th Century to Our Times, London, Bailliere, Tindall, and Cox, 1949.

Dubos, Rene and Jean, The White Plague—Tuberculosis, Man and Society, Boston, Little, Brown and Company, 1952.

"Experts Map TB Eradication Campaign," Medical World News, (September 15, 1965), pp. 30-31.

International Work in Tuberculosis, Geneva, World Health Organization, 1965.

Moorman, Lewis, J., "Our Knowledge of Tuberculosis: 4,000 Years' Accumulation—40 Years' Application," Transcript, Presidential Address, 40th Annual Meeting, National Tuberculosis Association, New York, National Tuberculosis Association, 1944.

Moorman, Lewis J., "Tuberculosis," in The History and Conquest of Common Diseases, edited by Walter Bett, Norman, University of Oklahoma Press, 1954, pp. 99-114.

Moorman, Lewis J., Tuberculosis and Genius, Chicago, University of Chicago Press, 1940.

"No Truce for Tuberculosis," subject of entire issue, World Health, (March, 1964).

Solomon, Paul, Tuberculosis, New York, Coward-McCann, 1952.

WHO Expert Committee on Tuberculosis, Eighth Report, World Health Organization Technical Report Series No. 290, 1964.

GLOSSARY

GLOSSARY OF SOME IMPORTANT
COMMUNICABLE DISEASE TERMS:

Acute—of short, severe duration.

Anaerobic—Growing only in absence of oxygen or air; as, anaerobic bacteria.

Antibody—Any serum globulin synthesized by lymphoid tissue as product of stimulus by an antigen.

Antigen—A substance that stimulates production of antibodies.

Arthropoda—A phylum of the animal kingdom made up of organisms with hard, jointed exoskeletons and paired, jointed legs. Among the arthropods are spiders and insects.

Auscultation—The act of listening for sounds or organs within the body (usually with a stethoscope) to determine their condition, chiefly lungs and hearts.

Bubo—A bulbous inflammation of a lymph gland in the groin or armpit. Seen after gonorrhea or syphilis.

Carrier—A person who harbors in his body specific infectious agents without showing any manifestations or discomforts of the infection. The person thus serves as a potential source of infection for others. His condition is known as a carrier state.

Chemoprophylaxis—The use of a chemical and/or antibiotic as means of preventing a specific disease, or halting progress of a disease which has begun but has not become manifest.

Chemotherapy—The use of chemicals and/or antibiotics as a means of treating a specific disease. The chemical agents affect causative organisms but do not harm patients.

Cirrhosis—A degenerative disease of the liver.

Clawhand—Atrophy and flexion of the hand; the fingers curl under giving appearance of claws. It occurs in leprosy and in syringomyelia. Also called *main en griffe*.

Communicable disease—An illness caused by a specific infectious agent or its toxic products capable of being transmitted from one person to another. Transmission is either direct

215

from an infected animal or person, or indirect via an inde-
terminate plant or animal host, a vector, or the inanimate
environment. (*Note:* For detailed explanation of direct and
indirect transmission, see chapter one.)

Communicable period—The time or times during which a communicable disease may be transmitted directly or indirectly from
man to man, man to animal, animal to man.

Contact—A person or animal known to have been sufficiently
near an infected person, animal, or environment to have
been exposed and possibly to have acquired a communicable
disease. Contacts are of two main types: (1) Direct, that is
involving physical touching, kissing, sexual intercourse. (2)
Indirect, meaning no physical contact. Infection is commun-
icated via some intervening medium. Airborne transmission
of smallpox is an example of indirect contact. (See chapter
one for more detailed explanation.)

Contamination—The presence of an infectious agent on a person's
body, and in or on objects, food, water, et cetera. *Note:*
Contamination is different from pollution, which refers to
presence of offensive but *noninfectious* matter in the environment.

Disinfection—A loose term meaning the destruction of infectious
agents outside the human body by chemical and/or physical
means, but not destruction of spores or microorganisms.
There are two general disinfection methods: (1) Concurrent
disinfection, that is, immediate destruction (usually by
burning) of infective materials from an infected person's
body. Also, immediate destruction of, or disinfection of,
articles touched by infective discharges. (2) Terminal disinfection. This is disinfection of a sick room and articles (sometimes complete destruction of things such as bed linen)
after the infected person is transferred to a hospital or dies.
Note: Terminal disinfection is falling from favor. Terminal
cleaning suffices. This is a scrubdown of the sickroom and
things touched by the sick person with hot water and soap
or detergent. Airing and sunning should follow. Further-
more, terminal cleaning is deemed necessary by many
authorities only for diseases spread by indirect contact.
Note: Steam sterilize all bedding after smallpox.

Emphysema—Swelling or ballooning of tissue due to presence
of air or gas. The condition appears frequently in diseased lungs.

Empyema—Presence of pus in pleural or other cavity.

Disinfestation—Extermination of insects, rodents, and other animal forms which might transmit infection and which are present upon the person, clothing, or in the environment. Disinfection is accomplished by physical and/or chemical means.

Endemic—The adjective applied to any disease habitually present within a given geographic area.

Epidemic—As a noun, an outbreak of any disease of high morbidity, occurring in a definite geographical area, clearly in excess of normal expectancy, and spreading rapidly. Single cases of communicable diseases long absent from a population, such as smallpox are considered a potential epidemic and handled as such. The word is derived from the Greek adjective *epidemios*, meaning prevalent.

Erythema—Redness of the skin produced by capillary congestion. It may result from a variety of causes.

Fatality—Death, but also an expression denoting rate of death among people suffering a particular disease. The term is generally expressed as a percentage of total cases. *Example:* Case fatality of smallpox is 40 per cent.

Fumigation—Destruction of animal forms by various gases or smoke.

Hemoglobinuria—Presence of hemoglobin (oxygen-carrying red blood cell pigment) in the urine.

Hematuria—The passing of blood in urine.

Host—Any plant or animal which harbors and nourishes another organism (or parasite) particularly an infectious agent. Hosts in which the parasite matures are primary or definitive hosts. Those in which the parasite passes its larval state are secondary or intermediate hosts.

Imagocide—An insecticide which kills insects in adult or imago, stages. Also called adulticide.

Immunity—Protection from, or resistance to, specific diseases granted by previous infection or immunization. (See chapter one.) Immunity is relative. Ordinarily effective protection may be overwhelmed by excessive doses of an infectious agent.

218   *Diseases that Plague Modern Man*

Incidence—The rate at which new cases of a particular disease occur. Incidence is generally expressed as number per 100,000 population per year.

Incubation—In communicable diseases, the time span of development of disease-producing microorganisms in man or vector.

Incubation period—Time elapsed between infection and appearance of first symptom of any disease.

Infection—Invasion of the body by an infectious agent, multiplication and development of same, and bodily reaction to its presence and toxins generated by it. An infection may be inapparent or manifest. *Note:* Infection should not be confused with contamination, which is the presence of an infective organism or organisms, on the body or on articles.

Infectious agent—Any organism capable of producing infection or infectious disease.

Infectious disease—Any disease of man or animal resulting from infection.

Infestation—Invasion of the body and clothing by arthropods, including mites and ticks. (See Arthropoda.)

Insecticide—Any chemical poisonous to arthropods; applied as powder, liquid, or spray. Insecticides usually possess long lasting, or residual, effect.

Isolation—Separation of persons with any communicable disease from other persons, usually for the period of communicability. The separation must be carried out in such places and under such conditions as will block direct or indirect transmission of infectious agents. Total isolation is necessary in dealing with some diseases (smallpox), has little or no beneficial effect in dealing with others (poliomyelitis).

Larvicide—An insecticide which kills arthropods in immature, or larval, stage.

Macule—A discolored spot on the skin, clearly distinguishable by color from its surrounding tissue, not elevated above the surface.

Micron—A metric unit of linear measure, expressed by the Greek letter *mu*. A micron is 1/1000 of a millimeter long.

Molluscicide—Any chemical used to destroy snails and other molluscs, generally by ingestion.

Morbidity—A term with several interrelated meanings in public health, the most common being the ratio of sick persons to well in a community, usually expressed in terms of cases per 100,000 population per year.

Mortality—The death rate; the ratio of total number of deaths to total number of population. General or crude mortality rate is usually stated in terms of number of deaths per 1,000 population per year. The disease-specific rate (deaths caused by any one disease), is the ratio of the number of deaths from one disease to total cases of it. Disease-specific mortality rates are usually expressed in number of deaths per 100,000 population per year.

Onset—The initial stage of invasion or attack, particularly of a communicable disease.

Papule—A small, distinctly defined, solid-feeling skin elevation or bump.

Paresis—A slight or incomplete paralysis.

Pathogen—A microorganism or material capable of causing disease.

Pathogenicity—The capacity of any infectious agent to produce pathologic changes or disease in any susceptible host.

Prevalence—The number of cases of any disease existing at a given time in a given geographic area. Prevalence is generally expressed as a ratio, that is, the number of active cases at a designated time per 100,000 population.

Pustule—A small, pus-filled skin elevation or bump.

Pyrexia—A fever.

Quarantine—A detention period applied to ships or persons from infected ports, generally 40 days long, but with exceptions. (1) Complete quarantine is detention and isolation of well persons and animals known or suspected to have been exposed to a communicable disease. Length of quarantine is equal to longest incubation period of the disease, and carried out in such manner as to prevent contact with those not exposed. (2) Modified quarantine is selective, partial limitation of movement of persons or animals to meet particular needs. *Example:* Exclusion of certain children from school because it is suspected they might transmit disease, but not exclusion from immediate family contact.

Rale—Any abnormal respiratory sound heard during auscultation, generally indicating some disease condition. From the
French *rale*, or rattle.

Recrudescence—The recurrence of symptoms after they have once
abated. (From the Latin verb *recrudescere*, to become sore
again.) The chief difference between a recrudescence and a
relapse is time. A recrudescence takes place after days or
weeks. A relapse takes place after weeks or months.

Reservoir—Any animal, man, plant, soil, or inanimate organic
matter in which an infectious agent lives and multiplies
preparatory to transmission to a susceptible host. Man is
the commonest reservoir of the diseases which afflict him.

Resistance—The term, as applied to communicable disease, means:
The natural ability of an individual to block invasion of, or
multiplication of, infectious agents, or to ward off their
dangerous and/or deadly effects. *Note:* The term resistance
also refers to ability to fight off deleterious effects of nox-
ious agents such as poisons, toxins, and irritants. (See chapter one, immunity.)

Rodenticide—Any agent used to destroy rodents, generally by
their ingestion of it.

Scrofula—A term formerly applied to several inflamed, oozing
conditions, now applied mostly to the tubercular deterioration of lymph glands of the neck.

Source of infection—Any persons, animal, object, or substance
from which an infectious agent passes to a victim. When a
disease is transmitted directly from a reservoir to a victim,
the reservoir is also the infection source. *Example:* measles.
Note: Source of infection is different from source of contamination or pollution such as an overflowing river, which
contaminates a public water supply.

Strain—Any group of organisms within a specific species or variety
which differ from the others by virtue of some singular
quality, as rough or smooth bacteria strains differ from
their companions.

Suppuration—Pus formation and loss.

Surveillance—There are two kinds: (1) Personal surveillance or
close observation and supervision of individual contacts of
of diseased persons to promptly detect fresh outbreaks, but
without restriction of individual personal movements. (2)

Disease surveillance. This is the continuing examination of all statistical and clinical aspects of any communicable disease which is spreading or threatening to spread.

Susceptible—Any person or animal not possessing either natural or artificial immunity to a particular communicable disease and therefore liable to contract the disease if exposed.

Suspect—Any person whose symptoms or medical history indicate he may be developing or may already have a communicable disease.

Vesicle—A small, clearly outlined skin blister filled to bursting with serous liquid.

NAME INDEX

SUBJECT INDEX